The

CLASSIC *f*M
PUZZLE
BOOK

An Hachette UK Company
www.hachette.co.uk

First published in Great Britain in 2019 by Cassell,
an imprint of Octopus Publishing Group Ltd
Carmelite House, 50 Victoria Embankment
London EC4Y 0DZ
www.octopusbooks.co.uk

ISBN 978 1 78840 138 8

A CIP catalogue record for this book is available from
the British Library.

Printed and bound in the United Kingdom

1 3 5 7 9 10 8 6 4 2

Senior Commissioning Editor: Joe Cottington
Assistant Editor: Emily Brickell
Art Editor: Geoff Fennell
Designer: Jeremy Tilston
Senior Production Controller: Allison Gonsalves
Product Management: Joel Stern, Emma Neary

The
CLASSIC *f*M
PUZZLE
BOOK

FOREWORD BY
ALEXANDER ARMSTRONG

MORE THAN 100
CLASSICAL CONUNDRUMS

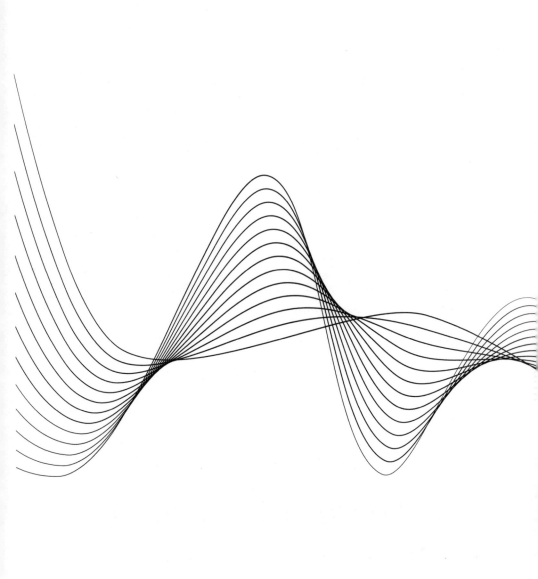

CONTENTS

FOREWORD

by

ALEXANDER ARMSTRONG

Congratulations! The very fact that you are reading this foreword places you in an infinitesimally small but statistically *extremely* high-achieving percentile of humanity. Not only are you holding a classical music puzzle book in your hands (in itself, a marker of exquisite erudition...) but within the set of People Who Like Classical Music Puzzles, you are that truly remarkable subset: People Who Actually Read the Forewords of Books. Your thirst for knowledge must be almost unslakeable and I genuinely worry for those against whom you will be pitting those quarrying wits.

The mental muscles that we must take particular care to exercise though, at all times and in all places, are those that hold *on* to knowledge, because they are the ones that we have cruelly neglected right from the moment we could fit a super computer the size of a pack of 20 Lambert & Butler cigarettes in our pockets. 'Use it or lose it' is the unbreakable rule if we want to keep our historic mental abilities. It's lovely that technology has taken up the slack on some of the more tedious brain functions (boring tasks like 'having to remember stuff', for example), but driving to the home of some friends for lunch the other day, I had to ring them and ask (like an idiot) for precise directions, because despite having been to their house *countless* times before, I had only ever done so while dumbly following the blessed satnav, under whose luxurious tyranny all ancient animal functions of navigation seem to have been switched off. And that, if we're not careful, is the general direction in which we are all heading, set to become spoiled princelings throwing away half-eaten sweetmeats having long since forgotten what the sweetmeat recipe was. Or something. But we mustn't get to the point where all knowledge just washes wantonly through our slack fingers, because it seems that while we've been whooping it up with our electronic encyclopedias falling open on precisely the desired page in our palms, our brains have quietly crept off to some distant cranial recess to sit on the sofa and eat chips.

What you are holding in your hands right now, as far as the brain is concerned, is a crisp green salad and a pair of running shoes.

On the pages that follow you will find questions to test all levels of classical music knowledge, which, by the way, makes this the perfect opportunity to assemble teams of all ages. The older team members can field some of the more solid, middle-of-the-bat questions about Beethoven and Andrew Lloyd Webber while the younger members can dive for the more flashy Thomas Adès and Yannick Nézet-Séguin balls. The result, however it is played, will be magnificent. As someone who spends a truly colossal amount of time 'at quiz', I can genuinely think of no more fruitful way of passing time with friends. And that's not because it's educational (although self-evidently it is precisely that). Nor is it because you are demonstrating some kind of weird, old-fashioned 'remembering facts' trick seldom seen outside niche circus acts these days (although yes, it's that too). It is simply because it draws and bonds people together by rewarding small personal victories, and revealing to us that we are still, at heart, intelligent beings.

Alexander Armstrong

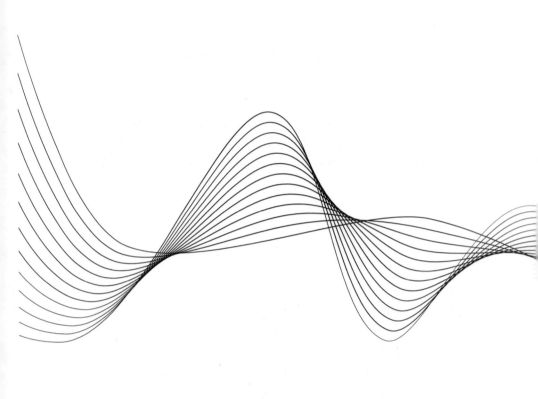

QUESTIONS

SECTION ONE

ADAGIO

(Italian: 'slow'.) A tempo instruction for music
to be played slowly. These puzzles will warm
up your brain without requiring any knowledge
of classical music.

PRESTO

Solution on page 194.

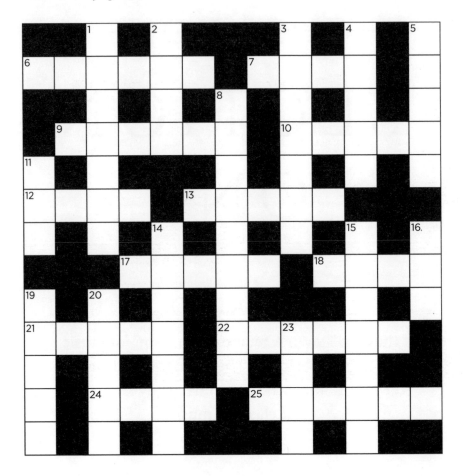

A classic quick crossword.

ACROSS

6   Festival, series of linked concerts (6)
7   Listen to (4)
9   Street musician (6)
10   - - - - - and rolls (5)
12   Study a musical score (4)
13   Group of singers (5)
17   Dramatic interval (5)
18   Individual performance (4)
21   Musical play (5)
22   Disc (6)
24   Pool for swans (4)
25   Wrote (6)

DOWN

1   Neither sharp nor flat (7)
2   Reserve a seat (4)
3   Chorus of a song (7)
4   Single piece of music on a CD (5)
5   Composer Philip (5)
8   Group of musicians (9)
11   Music, drawing or sculpture (3)
14   Singing to backing music (7)
15   High female voice (7)
16   Acknowledge the applause (3)
19   Audible sensation (5)
20   Campanologists ring them (5)
23   Backstage team (4)

SUDO-KEY

Solution on page 195.

mn				A		B		
	A				F		G	
E			mj		B		mn	C
			G					B
	E		D	B			C	
C				mj		mn		
D	mn			E	mj			A
	mj				A		B	
		A	C					

In this puzzle each block of nine squares must contain the letters of the keys A, B, C, D, E, F and G, along with mj to denote a major key and mn to denote a minor key. Every row (going across) and every column (going down) must contain nine different keys.

NOTATION

Solution on page 196.

Each letter that appears in the treble clef (A, B, C, D, E, F and G) has been replaced by a musical note. The other letters of the alphabet are in place. Can you work out the name of the composer and a piece of their music?

♪♪♪ T H O V ♪ N

♪♪♪♪ T ♪ L L ♪

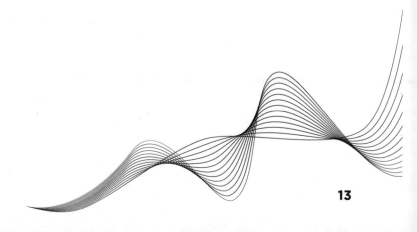

A CLASS ACT

Solution on page 196.

	Day					Starting time					Instrument				
	Monday	Tuesday	Wednesday	Thursday	Friday	11.00am	4.00pm	7.00pm	7.30pm	8.30pm	Cello	Drums	Saxophone	Trombone	Violin
Name Francesca															
Clara															
Franz															
Louise															
Carl															
Instrument Cello															
Drums															
Saxophone															
Trombone															
Violin															
Starting time 11.00am															
4.00pm															
7.00pm															
7.30pm															
8.30pm															

SECTION 1: ADAGIO

Five students at a music college have the option to learn a new musical instrument. They all choose different instruments. All classes meet on different days of the week and start at different times. From the clues given can you match each person with their chosen instrument and give the day and starting time of each session?

When you discover a positive piece of information that links things together, put a tick in the appropriate space in the grid. Put a cross in any space where you are sure there cannot be a link. Keep rereading the clues and adding ticks or crosses until you can work out the full solution.

CLUES

1   The saxophone class took place on a Wednesday. It began 30 minutes after the starting time for Francesca's class.
2   Franz went for Thursday's cello class. He originally wanted to learn to play the drums, but he thought that the morning starting time was too early.
3   Louise's Monday class had the latest of all starting times.
4   The violin class took place on Friday.
5   Carl's timetable was already quite full on Tuesday so he opted for a class on another day.

Name	Day	Starting time	Instrument

CYMBALISM

Solution on page 197.

Individual letters have been replaced by musical symbols. Name the four instruments depicted here. There are no cymbals to be seen!

MISSING VOICES

Solution on page 197.

The voices are Soprano, Alto, Tenor and Bass. The letters S, A, T and B (or some of these letters) are missing in the word below. Can you work out the title of the opera below?

F ? L ? ? ? F F

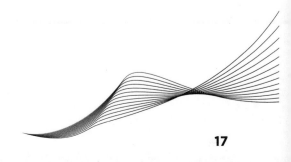

NUMBER NAMES

Solution on page 198.

Each letter has been given a numerical value from 1 to 6. The total value of each word is reached by adding up the individual letters. No two letters can have the same number.

R E G E R = 14

A I R = 15

E L G A R = 15

G R I E G = 16

A R I A = 19

What is the value of

A L L E G R I ?

BACH

Solution on page 198.

Fit all 28 listed words to fill the frame to make seven interlocking word squares. A word square reads the same whether read across or down. Bach appears four times, in four different word squares. The letters in his name are keyed in the grid to start you off. You could listen to the Goldberg Variations while solving this!

ABET	ECHO	IRIS
ADZE	EDIT	MOTH
AIRY	FISH	OBOE
AREA	HALF	STOP
BACH X 4	HERA	TEST
CELL	HERB	THOR
CRAM	HOPE	TOUR
CZAR	HYMN	
DARE	INTO	

THE CLASSIC FM HALL OF FAME

Solution on page 199.

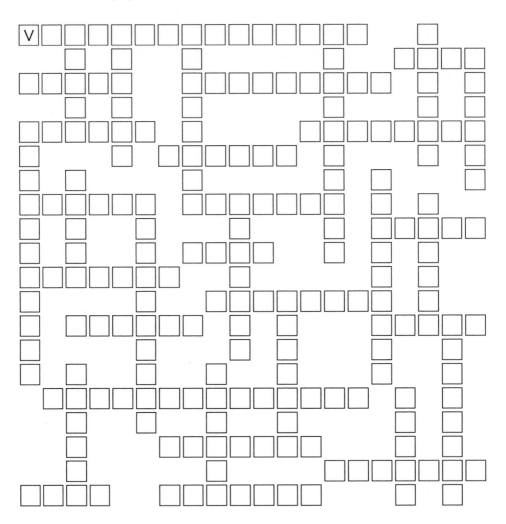

All the listed composers have appeared in the Classic FM Hall of Fame. Fit all the names back into the frame. Names read across or down. There's a one-letter start.

BACH
BARBER
BINGE
BORODIN
BUTTERWORTH
CHOPIN
COHEN
COPLAND
DELIUS
EINAUDI
ELGAR
GERSHWIN
GLASS

GOUNOD
HANDEL
HARVEY
HESS
HORNER
KORNGOLD
LAURIDSEN
MITCHELL
MUSSORGSKY
PACHELBEL
PART
RIMSKY-KORSAKOV
RODRIGO

ROSSINI
STRAUSS
STRAVINSKY
TALLIS
UNGAR
VAUGHAN WILLIAMS
WALTON
WIDOR
WILLIAMS
WISEMAN
ZIMMER

SCREEN TEST

Solution on page 200.

```
T  U  S  A  I  K  I  N  I  C  N  A  M  H  X
B  H  C  E  V  O  K  E  R  H  S  O  E  M  J
S  A  E  X  T  B  O  E  V  S  R  R  S  O  N
M  H  C  F  T  A  S  A  S  R  R  R  H  Z  O
A  V  O  H  A  R  O  E  I  M  E  N  I  A  V
I  R  B  R  O  V  H  C  A  T  E  M  E  R  O
L  O  A  H  E  R  O  N  S  D  M  T  D  T  N
L  T  R  R  E  N  N  U  K  E  B  A  A  T  I
I  A  R  N  E  Z  B  E  R  N  S  T  E  I  N
W  I  Y  T  N  T  R  P  R  I  X  O  R  T  A
A  D  L  U  S  T  A  H  A  R  T  R  E  A  M
L  A  B  O  R  O  D  I  N  W  C  E  R  N  H
T  L  H  A  R  R  Y  P  O  T  T  E  R  I  C
O  G  T  X  O  D  N  A  R  G  E  L  A  C  A
N  S  M  A  H  L  E  R  S  E  N  O  J  E  R
```

The names of movies with a famous soundtrack, and people who have contributed music to movies are hidden in the word square on the left. All words are in straight lines and can go horizontally, vertically or diagonally. They may read forward or backward.

BACH	HORNER	ROTA
BARRY	JARRE	SHORE
BERNSTEIN	JOHN	SHREK
BORODIN	JONES	STAR TREK
COATES	LEGRAND	THE FAVOURITE
GHOSTBUSTERS	MAHLER	TITANIC
GLADIATOR	MANCINI	WALTON
HARRY POTTER	MORRICONE	WAR HORSE
HART	MOZART	WILLIAMS
HERRMANN	RACHMANINOV	ZIMMER
HESS	READE	

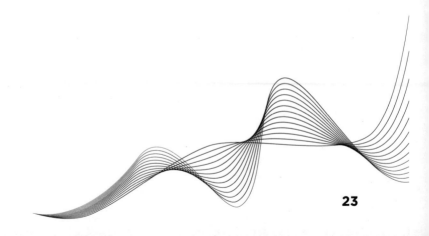

CYMBALISM

Solutions on page 201.

Individual letters have been replaced by musical symbols. Name the four musical terms depicted here.

MISSING VOICES

Solution on page 201.

The voices are Soprano, Alto, Tenor and Bass. The letters S, A, T and B (or some of these letters) are missing in the word below. Can you work out the title of the opera below?

? O ? C ?

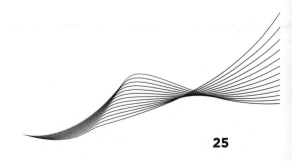

RAFFLE PRIZES

Solution on page 202.

A music appreciation society held a raffle. There were four prizes, all of which were tickets to a different concert. The winning numbers were 048, 085, 126 and 197. All the winning raffle tickets were different in colour.

A visit to a violin concert was won by the owner of a pink ticket that had an odd number on it.

Tickets to a classical guitar recital were one of the prizes but it was not the one won by the owner of a green ticket.

Only the white ticket had a lower number on it than the ticket that claimed the tickets for a piano recital.

The blue ticket had a higher number than the ticket that landed the prize of a ticket to an evening of choral music.

Can you work out the winning number and the ticket colour for each prize?

ADDERS

Solution on page 202.

What do you get if you add an insect to the edge of a garment?

Answer: _____

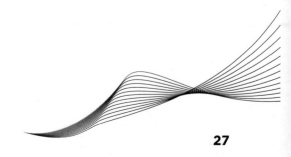

MAJOR SEVENTH

Solution on page 203.

The listed classical music-linked words all contain seven letters. Fit them all in the frame to read either across or down. One letter is keyed in.

ADIEMUS
BAROQUE
BASSOON
BEECHAM
BORODIN
CADENCE

COMPOSE
EINAUDI
FIDELIO
GAVOTTE
GORECKI
PASSAGE

QUARTET
REQUIEM
RUSALKA
STRINGS

NOTATION

Solution on page 204.

Each letter that appears in the treble clef (A, B, C, D, E, F and G) has been replaced by a musical note. The other letters of the alphabet are in place. Can you work out the name of the composer and a piece of their music?

O ♪ ♪ ♪ N ♪ ♪ ♪ H
L ♪/♪ ♪ L L ♪/H ♪ L ♪ N ♪

MUSIC MAKERS

Solution on page 204.

From the information in the pictures and the things said, name each performer, match them to their instrument and decide how many years they have been playing.

MISSING VOICES

Solution on page 205.

The voices are Soprano, Alto, Tenor and Bass. The letters S, A, T and B (or some of these letters) are missing in the word below. Can you work out the title of the opera below?

? L U E ? E ? R D' ? / C ? ? ? L E

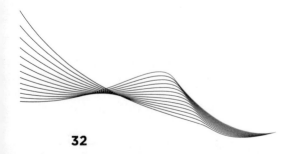

NOTATION

Solution on page 205.

Each letter that appears in the treble clef (A, B, C, D, E, F and G) has been replaced by a musical note. The other letters of the alphabet are in place. Can you work out the name of the composer and a piece of their music?

♪ ♪ R ♪ ♪ R

♪ O V ♪ R/♪ ♪ ♪ ♪ H

RING CYCLE

Solution on page 206.

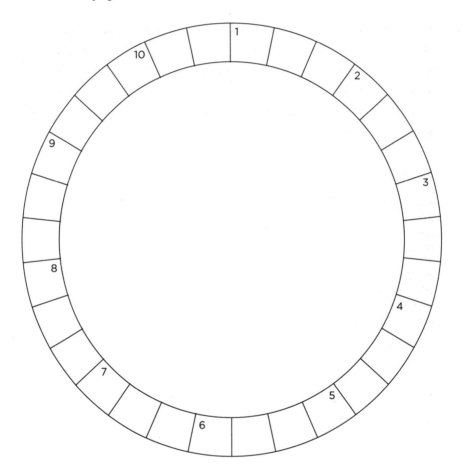

Solve the clues below, which are in no particular order, and slot the five-letter answers into their correct places in the ring. The last two letters of each answer form the first two of the next. Answer 1 is the musical instrument. Answer 5 forms a musical link with answer 1. The remaining clues are general in nature, and there is only one way to complete the ring cycle.

CLUES
Interior design
Musical instrument
Stoned fruit
Lukewarm
Indirect comment
Original thoughts
Vocalists
Heavenly being
Angry
Run away to marry

M FOR MUSIC

Solution on page 207.

```
T  M  H  O  A  L  S  A  R  R  E  K  C  A  M
Z  A  C  L  M  A  G  I  C  F  L  U  T  E  X
D  E  R  R  V  G  M  U  T  T  E  R  H  I  M
O  S  A  L  T  I  O  A  N  I  C  T  M  I  L
B  T  M  E  N  R  Z  Y  R  G  A  E  N  M  N
M  R  T  U  Z  D  A  Q  U  I  L  I  E  A  H
A  O  E  O  T  A  R  E  D  O  M  S  G  S  O
M  T  V  J  O  M  T  R  D  I  S  B  G  C  S
S  A  V  E  A  L  E  I  N  I  J  O  A  A  S
A  B  N  H  M  V  C  S  A  I  O  E  P  G  L
C  L  L  D  E  E  T  E  S  M  H  T  R  N  E
A  E  X  T  O  R  N  K  U  I  O  U  O  I  D
R  M  N  B  E  L  O  T  Y  U  A  M  N  Z  N
A  O  U  L  A  C  I  S  U  M  L  H  I  E  E
M  E  Z  Z  O  T  E  N  E  S  S  A  M  Y  M
```

A medley of words with a music link – composers, conductors, works, instruments and more – are hidden in the word square on the left. All words are in straight lines and can go horizontally, vertically or diagonally. They may read forward or backward.

MACKERRAS
MADRIGAL
MAESTRO
MAGIC FLUTE
MAHLER
MAMBO
MANDOLIN
MARACAS
MARCH
MARIMBA
MASCAGNI
MASSENET

MEHTA
MELBA
MELODIC
MENDELSSOHN
MENUHIN
MESSIAEN
MESSIAH
MEZZO
MINIM
MINOR
MINSTREL
MINUET

MODERATO
MONTEVERDI
MOOG
MOTET
MOVEMENT
MOZART
MUSICAL
MUTE
MUTI
MUTTER

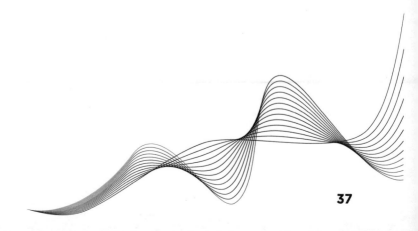

INSTRUMENTAL

Solution on page 208.

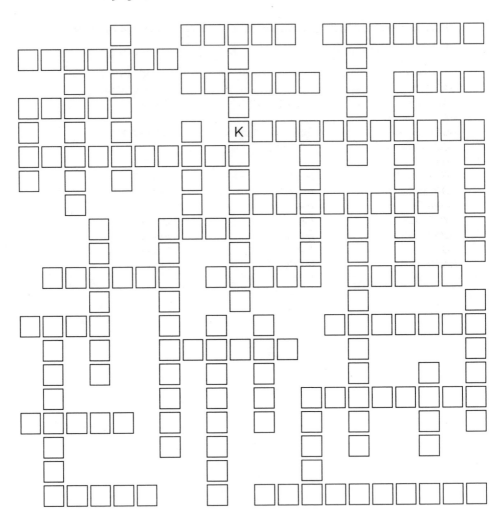

Fit all the listed instruments into the frame. Words read across or down. There's a one-letter start.

BAGPIPES
BANJO
BASSOON
BUGLE
CELLO
CHIMES
CITTERN
COR ANGLAIS
CORNET
CYMBALS
GLOCKENSPIEL
GUITAR
HARMONICA

HARP
HARPSICHORD
HORN
HURDYGURDY
KETTLEDRUMS
KOTO
LUTE
LYRES
MARIMBA
OBOE
OCARINA
PIANO
PICCOLO

SAXOPHONE
SHAWM
SITAR
SPINET
TABOR
TAMBOURINE
THEORBO
TROMBONE
VIOLA
VIOLIN
VIRGINAL
ZITHER

CYMBALISM

Solutions on page 209.

Individual letters have been replaced by musical symbols. Start with an instrument and discover the other words with a musical link.

SUDO-KEY

Solution on page 210.

		E	C	mj			G	D
			D			mn		E
mn							mj	
E		B			mj			
	D							A
A	mn			E	B	mj		
		F						
B			mn		A			mj
						B		

In this puzzle each block of nine squares must contain the letters of the keys A, B, C, D, E, F and G, along with mj to denote a major key and mn to denote a minor key. Every row (going across) and every column (going down) must contain nine different keys.

OPERA IN THE PARK

Solution on page 211.

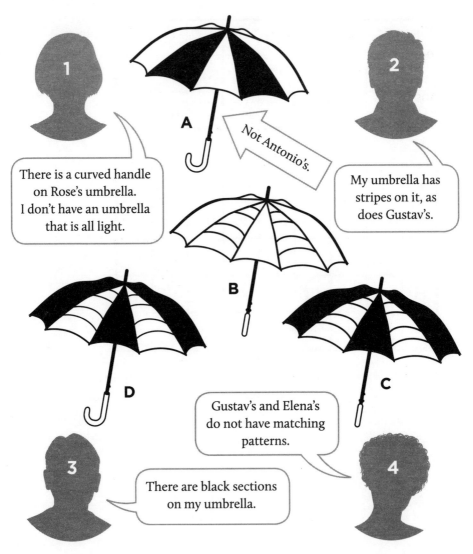

There is a curved handle on Rose's umbrella. I don't have an umbrella that is all light.

Not Antonio's.

My umbrella has stripes on it, as does Gustav's.

Gustav's and Elena's do not have matching patterns.

There are black sections on my umbrella.

Four friends have gone to enjoy an outdoor music concert on a summer evening. Naturally, they each take along an umbrella. From the information in the pictures and the things said, match the people, 1 to 4, to the umbrellas, A to D.

ADDERS

Solution on page 211.

What do you get if you add a computer virus to a French word for 'the'?

Answer: _____

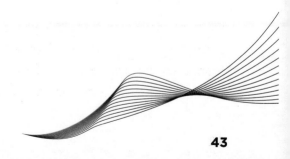

MAJOR SEVENTH

Solution on page 212.

The listed classical music-linked words all contain seven letters. Fit them all in the frame to read either across or down. One letter is keyed in.

BALLADE
CLASSIC
DELIBES
FIDDLER
JUPITER
KARAJAN

LISTENS
LULLABY
MARIMBA
OCTAVES
PASSION
PIE JESU

RODRIGO
ROMANCE
SEGOVIA
SINGING

NUMBER NAMES

Solution on page 213.

Each letter has been given a numerical value from 1 to 6. The total value of each word is reached by adding up the individual letters. No two letters can have the same number.

A N O N = 9

T O N E = 10

N O T E S = 16

S E A S O N = 24

What is the value of

S O N A T A?

STUDENT SHARE

Solution on page 213.

A group of nine students, all studying for a degree in music, share a rambling old Victorian house. There are three rooms on each of the three floors, so everyone has their own room.

The staircase is on the left of the house.

There is at least one woman living on every floor, but there are no two people whose names begin with the same initial on a floor.

Sergei and Elizabeth are on different floors.

Diana has Sofia's room directly above her and Maurice's room directly below. Peter's room is next to Diana's.

Nikolai goes past two rooms to get to his, and Mikhail is next door to him.

Julia is the only girl to have to walk past another girl's room to reach her own.

Who is in each room?

NOTATION

Solution on page 214.

Each letter that appears in the treble clef (A, B, C, D, E, F and G) has been replaced by a musical note. The other letters of the alphabet are in place. Can you work out the name of the composer and a piece of their music?

♪♪♪♪

♪♪♪♪H♪N♪L♪

ADDERS

Solution on page 214.

What do you get if you add history to a word meaning spoken?

Answer: _____

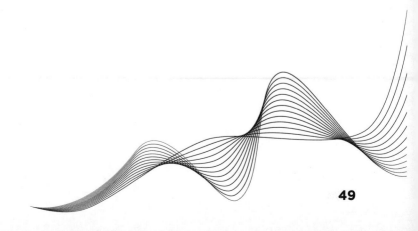

CONDUCTORS

Solution on page 215.

```
I  U  L  M  A  A  Z  E  L  I  K  I  W  Z  I
T  T  X  E  L  T  T  A  R  W  S  T  O  X  X
J  K  L  B  M  I  L  L  O  R  I  B  R  A  B
B  L  N  O  M  A  R  O  V  O  Z  E  D  G  E
H  E  S  I  S  K  D  X  T  U  N  B  S  Y  E
A  M  R  U  T  G  N  U  Y  I  Q  U  W  V  C
N  P  S  N  L  I  D  U  D  A  L  S  O  P  H
I  E  I  O  S  X  A  R  S  L  O  N  R  P  A
V  R  V  U  R  T  A  H  T  S  K  O  T  O  M
E  E  A  E  L  G  E  N  C  A  E  T  H  U  W
R  R  D  U  T  Y  E  I  R  P  O  N  Z  I  M
P  L  O  O  D  G  R  A  N  N  H  A  L  L  E
E  B  I  V  R  A  J  N  I  E  L  S  E  N  T
X  L  O  A  Z  A  S  T  O  K  O  W  S  K  I
E  D  S  U  N  M  I  O  B  N  E  R  A  B  L
```

The names of an array of wielders of the baton are hidden in the word square on the left. All words are in straight lines and can go horizontally, vertically or diagonally. They may read forward or backward.

ALSOP	ELIOT GARDINER	ORAMO
BARBIROLLI	GLOVER	PREVIN
BARENBOIM	HAITINK	RATTLE
BEECHAM	HALLE	SARGENT
BERNSTEIN	JARVI	SOLTI
BOULT	KLEMPERER	STOKOWSKI
DAVIS	KNUSSEN	VON KARAJAN
DUDAMEL	MAAZEL	WILSON
DUTOIT	NIELSEN	WOOD
ELDER	NOTT	WORDSWORTH

CHOIR PRACTICE

Solution on page 216.

¹B	²	³	⁴		⁵	⁶A	⁷	⁸
A						L		
S						T		
⁹	¹⁰	¹¹A	¹²S		¹³	¹⁴	¹⁵	¹⁶			¹⁷	¹⁸	¹⁹A	²⁰

(Grid as shown with interlocking word squares)

Fit all 28 listed words to fill the frame to make seven interlocking word squares. A word square reads the same whether read across or down. It's choir practice. There are two men from the bass section and five women who all sing alto. The one tenor is away and, of course, the sopranos are always late. Our seven singers are already in place in the grid.

ALAS	POPE	SOWN
AREA	RILL	STEW
IRON	SALT	STAR
LULL	SELL	STOP
MASS	SLOB	TIPS
PLOD	SNOW	TRAP
POLO	SORT	WASP

SUDO-KEY

Solution on page 217.

	mn		D		B			F
A						C		
			G	mj			B	
		C			mj	B		D
G			C	A				mn
E		D	F			A		
	G			mn	C			
		mj						A
B			A		E		G	

In this puzzle each block of nine squares must contain the letters of the keys A, B, C, D, E, F and G, along with mj to denote a major key and mn to denote a minor key. Every row (going across) and every column (going down) must contain nine different keys.

ON TOUR

Solution on page 218.

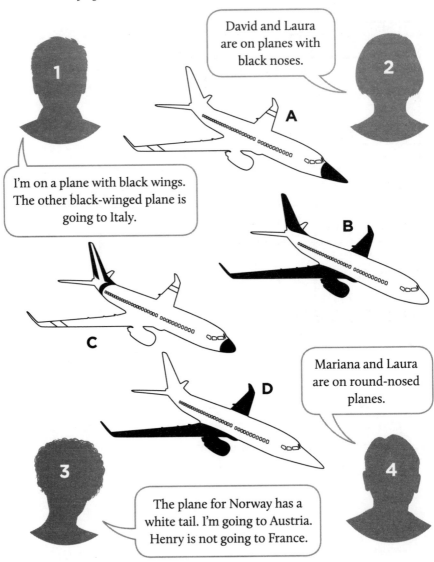

David and Laura are on planes with black noses.

I'm on a plane with black wings. The other black-winged plane is going to Italy.

Mariana and Laura are on round-nosed planes.

The plane for Norway has a white tail. I'm going to Austria. Henry is not going to France.

Four famous singers are travelling to perform in concert. From the information in the pictures and the things said, match each performer to their plane and decide on their country of destination.

NUMBER NAMES

Solution on page 218.

Each letter has been given a numerical value from 1 to 7. The total value of each word is reached by adding up the individual letters. No two letters can have the same number.

L A R G O = 15

A L L E G R O = 22

L E G A T O = 26

What is the value of

A L L E G R E T T O ?

NOTATION

Solution on page 219.

Each letter that appears in the treble clef (A, B, C, D, E, F and G) has been replaced by a musical note. The other letters of the alphabet are in place. Can you work out the name of the composer and a piece of their music?

W ♪♪♪ R

O ♪♪ R O N

ADDERS

Solution on page 219.

What do you get if you add part of a fish to beer?

Answer: _____

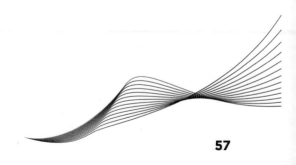

MAJOR SEVENTH

Solution on page 220.

The listed classical music-linked words all contain seven letters. Fit them all in the frame to read either across or down. One letter is keyed in.

ALLEGRI
ANDANTE
CYMBALS
DISCORD
EMPEROR
MELODIC

PLAYING
RAGTIME
ROSSINI
SMETANA
STRAUSS
STUDIES

TOCCATA
TRILLED
TRUMPET
WRITERS

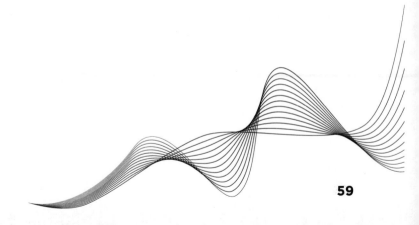

QUIZ NIGHT

Solution on page 221.

The players and staff of a large orchestra have staged their annual quiz night.

Five teams have taken part, with their monikers giving a hint of their musical affinity. Each team chose a specialist subject on which they were asked questions.

Best Batons did not quite live up to their name and finished fourth.

The Baroque Chicks did not take film music as a special subject.

The team answering questions on Elgar finished directly above the team called The Fiddlers, who in turn were directly above the team who chose Purcell as their specialist subject.

Only the Russian music specialists finished above the team called No Strings.

The Timps were two positions below the team answering questions about Mozart.

Can you match finishing positions to the teams and their specialist subjects?

MUSIC BOXES

Solution on page 221.

Fit all 28 listed words to fill the frame to make seven interlocking word squares. A word square reads the same whether read across or down. A musical instrument appears in each word square.
To start you off, TUBA appears in position 2 in the grid.

AGOG	ITEM	RISE
ASIA	LUTE	ROBE
CROP	LYRE	SAGE
DRUM	MASH	SLIP
EBBS	MESS	TOLD
EGGS	OBOE	TUBA
ENDS	PATS	UPON
GONG	PEEL	USES
HARP	PEST	
IRIS	RIOT	

MISSING VOICES

Solution on page 222.

The voices are Soprano, Alto, Tenor and Bass. The letters S, A, T and B (or some of these letters) are missing in the word below. Can you work out the title of the opera below?

L ? / ? R ? V I ? ? ?

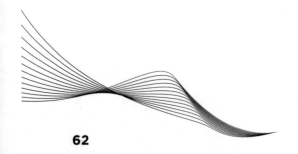

ADDERS

Solution on page 222.

What do you get if you add a stumble to rented properties?

Answer: _____

UNFINISHED SYMPHONY

Solution on page 223.

```
A  T  L  E  N  I  N  G  R  A  D  J  A  N  X
P  L  A  U  G  C  H  O  R  W  S  O  A  L  I
O  N  R  Q  O  U  L  A  D  P  H  I  N  N  M
C  N  O  I  T  C  E  R  R  U  S  E  R  A  R
A  Z  H  T  H  B  A  I  C  S  C  V  N  Z  E
L  A  C  E  I  M  N  L  U  L  H  E  R  N  T
Y  D  O  H  C  G  O  R  L  N  O  U  I  V  I
P  R  U  T  X  C  E  E  A  E  O  P  L  T  P
T  U  N  A  K  L  W  I  R  L  L  U  S  Y  U
I  M  O  P  T  E  L  O  O  A  M  U  T  T  J
C  R  Y  T  R  A  I  C  T  J  A  J  I  A  N
D  O  I  A  T  C  B  U  S  F  S  F  O  A  T
T  L  F  I  A  C  I  G  A  R  T  X  I  N  S
P  L  O  N  D  O  N  R  P  U  E  D  U  R  G
N  O  I  T  A  M  R  O  F  E  R  H  A  Z  E
```

The names of symphonies are hidden in the word square on the left. All words are in straight lines and can go horizontally, vertically or diagonally. They may read forward or backward. However, the work is unfinished as there is one name which does *not* appear in the grid. Which one is it?

ALLELUIA	FAUST	PASTORAL
ALPINE	FIRE	PATHETIQUE
APOCALYPTIC	GOTHIC	REFORMATION
BEAR	HEN	RESURRECTION
CHORAL	HUNT	SCHOOLMASTER
CLOCK	ITALIAN	SPRING
COLOUR	JUPITER	SURPRISE
DRUMROLL	LENINGRAD	TOY
EROICA	LITTLE RUSSIAN	TRAGIC
FAREWELL	LONDON	

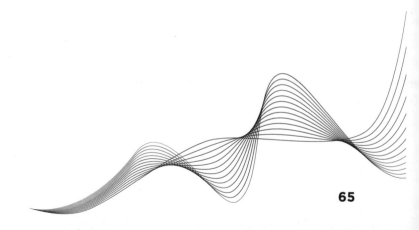

NUMBER NAMES

Solution on page 224.

Each letter has been given a numerical value from 1 to 7. The total value of each word is reached by adding up the individual letters. No two letters can have the same number.

S A T I E = 20

M A S S = 25

M E S S I A E N = 33

M A S S E N E T = 36

What is the value of

S A I N T - S A E N S ?

SUDO-KEY

Solution on page 225.

	F					G		B
D								
		E		F	C	A	D	
			B					E
		F	E	C	A	D		
B				mj				
	C	G	A		D	mn		
								G
F		mn					mj	

In this puzzle each block of nine squares must contain the letters of the keys A, B, C, D, E, F and G, along with mj to denote a major key and mn to denote a minor key. Every row (going across) and every column (going down) must contain nine different keys.

MUSICAL MEMORABILIA

Solution on page 226.

	Lot number					Item					Price				
	12	17	21	42	59	Books	Poster	Sheet music	T-shirts	Vinyl records	£10	£20	£30	£60	£100
Name Florence															
Claude															
Heather															
Johann															
Lili															
Price £10															
£20															
£30															
£60															
£100															
Item Books															
Poster															
Sheet music															
T-shirts															
Vinyl records															

An auction offers musical memorabilia. Five friends go along. Each of them bids and purchases a single item. The five items bought are different in type and go for a different hammer price. From the clues given can you match all the information together?

When you discover a positive piece of information that links things together, put a tick in the appropriate space in the grid. Put a cross in any space where you are sure there cannot be a link. Keep rereading the clues and adding ticks or crosses until you can work out the full solution.

CLUES

1 Florence bought some sheet music which cost more than the poster but less than the T-shirts.
2 Heather was the last one to buy anything.
3 The item with the lowest lot number fetched the lowest price.
4 Lot 21 was the vinyl records. Johann's books cost five times that amount.
5 None of the women bought items with even lot numbers.

Name	Lot number	Item	Price

ADDERS

Solution on page 226.

What do you get if you add a vehicle to fellows?

Answer: _____

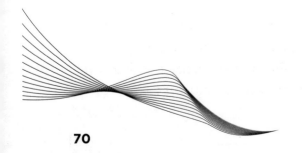

JUST THE TICKET

Solution on page 227.

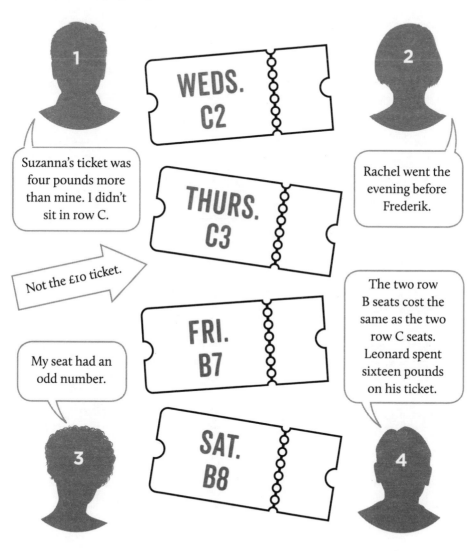

Suzanna's ticket was four pounds more than mine. I didn't sit in row C.

WEDS. C2

Rachel went the evening before Frederik.

THURS. C3

Not the £10 ticket.

FRI. B7

The two row B seats cost the same as the two row C seats. Leonard spent sixteen pounds on his ticket.

My seat had an odd number.

SAT. B8

Four friends visit a concert hall. They go on different nights, and sit in different seats which were all at different prices. From the information in the pictures and the things said, name each person, match them to their tickets and say what each ticket cost.

THE SHOW MUST GO ON

Solution on page 228.

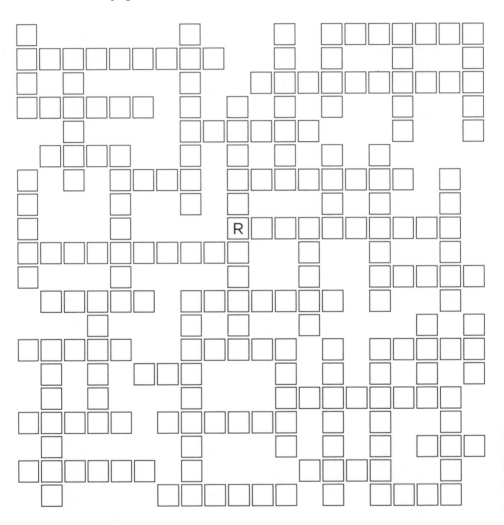

The listed words are linked to live performances. Fit them into the frame. Words read across or down. There's a one-letter start.

ACT
APPEARS
APPLAUSE
ARTISTRY
AUDITORIUM
CASTS
CHORUS
CLASSIC
CREW
DANCERS
DIVA
DUET
ENCORE

ENTERTAINS
EVENT
EXTRA
FAN
FESTIVAL
GROUPS
HEAR
LIGHTS
MAESTRO
NEW
NEXT
OPENS
OPERA

ORCHESTRA
OVATION
PERFORMANCE
POSTER
PRESS
REHEARSALS
ROLES
SALES
SCENES
SEATS
SEES
SINGERS
SONG

SPEAK
SPOTLIGHT
STAGE
STALLS
STARS
THEATRE
TICKET
TOURING
TRIO

ON CUE

Solution on page 229.

Five people are in line to buy CDs.

Everyone is being patient, but both Johannes and Isabella are really in a hurry to be served. Each person has purchased different CDs. For example, one shopper has only bought Puccini's *La Bohème*.

£12, £16, £20, £32 and £40 are the different amounts the people in line will have to pay.

The lady who bought choir music stands directly in front of the person who spent £20 on opera arias and duets.

Rosie has £12 worth of items. She is not fourth in line.

The person who is last in the line spent the most. They did not buy the film soundtrack.

Thea, who is second in the line, spent twice as much as the man who is into Vivaldi's *Four Seasons*.

Edward is in the middle of the line.

Can you put the people in order in the line, name them and say how much they have spent and on what type of music?

NOTATION

Solution on page 229.

Each letter that appears in the treble clef (A, B, C, D, E, F and G) has been replaced by a musical note. The other letters of the alphabet are in place. Can you work out the name of the composer and a piece of their music?

♪♪ X

T H ♪ / ♪ ♪ R ♪ ♪ N / O ♪ / ♪ ♪ N ♪

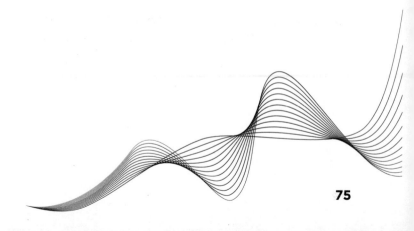

SPOT THE DIFFERENCE

Solution on page 230.

Can you find ten things in the left picture that do not appear in the right one?

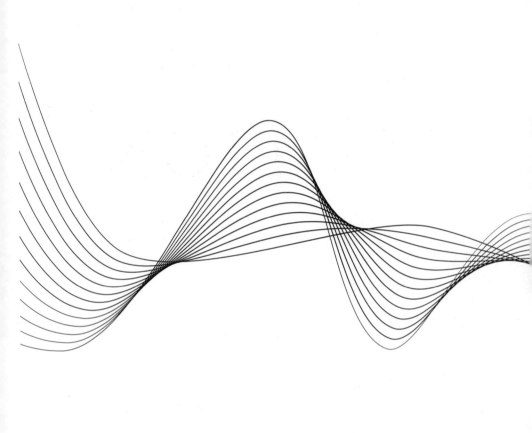

QUESTIONS

SECTION TWO

~

ACCELERANDO

(Italian: 'getting faster'.) A little knowledge
of classical music will come in handy here,
but you do not need to be an expert.

CODA: HARP

Solution on page 234.

4	■	13	■	2	5	4	2	3	2	10	11	5
¹H	²A	³R	⁴P	■	12	■	9	■	8	■	4	■
6	■	4	■	■	14	15	16	14	3	7	13	3
5	4	1	14	3	14	■	7	■	14	■	9	■
7	■	2	■	■	20	■	21	■	■	4	■	17
8	2	9	18	6	■	4	11	3	4	13	5	14
7	■	2	■	■	19	14	14	■	■	16	■	26
2	12	10	14	25	3	2	■	5	1	2	3	14
9	■	14	■	■	14	■	5	■	■	5	■	12
■	13	■	24	■	14	■	26	14	2	5	14	12
14	23	25	14	22	22	12	14	■	■	7	■	14
■	7	■	7	■	14	■	2	■	4	11	3	3
7	16	7	9	14	3	2	3	6	■	23	■	6

The HARP clue box is filled: ¹H ²A ³R ⁴P

Each letter of the alphabet has been replaced by a number. Work out which number represents which letter to complete the crossword-style grid which has words reading across and down. You have the letters in the word HARP to start you off.

Fill in the 1 to 26 grid with letters of the alphabet as you discover them.

1	2	3	4	5	6	7	8	9	10	11	12	13
14	15	16	17	18	19	20	21	22	23	24	25	26

When you have cracked the code, the letters 18, 13, 9, 7, 22, 14, 16, 16, 7 spell out a composer who used the instrument in a solo from one of his operas.

18	13	9	7	22	14	16	16	7

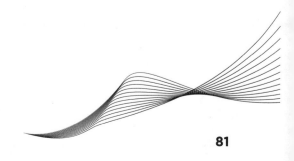

RING CYCLE

Solution on page 235.

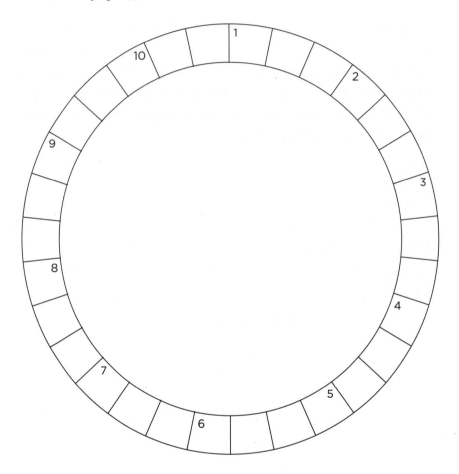

SECTION 2: ACCELERANDO

Solve the clues below, which are in no particular order, and slot the five-letter answers into their correct places in the ring. The last two letters of each answer form the first two of the next. Answer 1 is the Italian composer. Answer 5 forms a musical link with answer 1. The remaining clues are general in nature, and there is only one way to complete the ring cycle.

CLUES
Lilac colour
Italian composer
Large box for treasure
Musical play
Start a point in tennis
Delicious cooking smell
Part of a poem
Bend down
Trench
System that locates cars, aircraft, ships, etc.

COMPOSER OR PASTA?

Solutions on page 235.

Think you can tell your pasta from your composers? It's time to put your knowledge to the test. Decide if each word is the name of a composer or a type of pasta.

1   Tuffoli

2   Bertoncini

3   Bucatini

4   Sorprese

5   Capellini

6   Testaroli

7   Piccinni

8   Zitoni

9   Filini

10 Mercadante

11 Pizzetti

12 Pinottini

13 Dragonetti

14 Campagnoli

15 Bazzini

HIDDEN INSTRUMENT

Solution on page 236.

Which musical instrument is hidden in the sentence below? Discover it by joining words or parts of words together.

I LOVE A WALTZ, IT HERALDS MY FAVOURITE PART OF A MUSICAL EVENING!

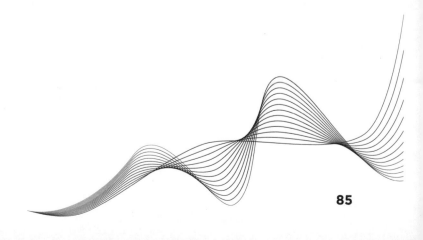

PRESTO

Solution on page 236.

A classic quick crossword.

ACROSS

6 Home city of the Wigmore Hall (6)
7 Leading lady (4)
9 Composer of *Lohengrin* (6)
10 He wrote *Sea Pictures* (5)
12 Low female voice (4)
13 Academy Award (5)
17 Scandinavian composer Edvard (5)
18 Ancient stringed instrument (4)
21 Guitarist Julian (5)
22 Strauss's favourite river (6)
24 Poet used by Britten in his *War Requiem* (4)
25 Gramophone needle (6)

DOWN

1 At a walking pace (7)
2 Wind instrument (4)
3 Composer Debbie (7)
4 Slow piece of music (5)
5 Book of words and music (5)
8 Getting louder (9)
11 English composer Arnold (3)
14 Brass instrument (7)
15 Part of the percussion section (7)
16 *The Flight of the Bumble* - - - (3)
19 Instruments with reeds (5)
20 José Carreras, for example (5)
23 Musical sound (4)

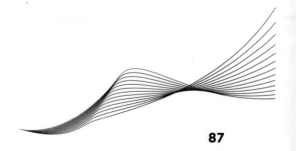

COMPOSITION

Solution on page 237.

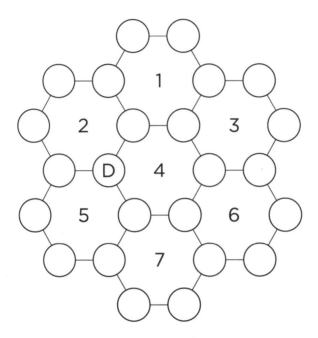

Fit the listed words into the frame, using the key letter as a starter. One letter goes in each circle, and words are written clockwise around a number. When all the words are in place, the addition of two letters will fill the grid and form the name of a composer.

AZTECS	DEMAND	SCHEME
DAMNED	ERASED	TRENDY

CYMBALISM

Solutions on page 238.

Individual letters have been replaced by musical symbols. Name the four words depicted here. They all have a musical link.

CAN YOU GUESS THE OPERA FROM THE EMOJIS?

Solutions on page 238.

Using only emojis, we've tried to describe the hideously complex and emotional plots of 11 operas. Can you work out which is which?

1.

a) *Beatrice and Benedict*
b) *The Marriage of Figaro*
c) *Eugene Onegin*
d) *Hansel and Gretel*

2.

a) *Carmen*
b) *Eugene Onegin*
c) *Madam Butterfly*
d) *Così Fan Tutte*

3.

a) *La Traviata*
b) *The Barber of Seville*
c) *The Marriage of Figaro*
d) *La Donna del Lago*

4.

a) *Turandot*
b) *The Mikado*
c) *Tosca*
d) *Madam Butterfly*

5.

a) *The Cunning Little Vixen*
b) *A Midsummer Night's Dream*
c) *The Fairy Queen*
d) *The Tales of Hoffmann*

6.

a) *The Fairy Queen*
b) *The Coronation of Poppea*
c) *Tristan and Isolde*
d) *Solomon*

7.

a) *La Cenerentola*
b) *A Midsummer Night's Dream*
c) *The Tales of Hoffmann*
d) *Hansel and Gretel*

8.

a) *The Cunning Little Vixen*
b) *La Traviata*
c) *La Cenerentola*
d) *The Magic Flute*

9.

a) *Don Giovanni*
b) *Così Fan Tutte*
c) *Carmen*
d) *L'Elisir d'Amore*

10.

a) *La Bohème*
b) *Norma*
c) *La Traviata*
d) *Tosca*

11.

a) *Il Trovatore*
b) *Dido and Aeneas*
c) *Orphée et Eurydice*
d) *Aida*

RING CYCLE

Solution on page 239.

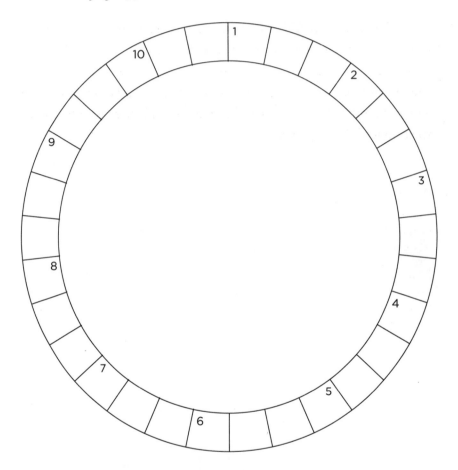

Solve the clues below, which are in no particular order, and slot
the five-letter answers into their correct places in the ring. The last
two letters of each answer form the first two of the next. Answer 1 is
the Puccini opera. Answer 5 is another opera, by a French composer.
The remaining clues are general in nature, and there is only one way
to complete the ring cycle.

CLUES
Opera by Puccini premiered in 1900
Glossy
Man-made waterway
Picture taken with a camera
Restraint for a dog
First word of the Greek alphabet
Chief port of Israel on the Mediterranean coast
Legendary character said to have sold his soul to the devil
Mythological spirit
Not fresh, past its best

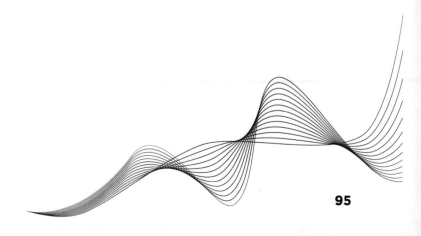

CAN YOU PUT THE INSTRUMENT IN ITS RIGHT PLACE IN THE ORCHESTRA?

Solution on page 239.

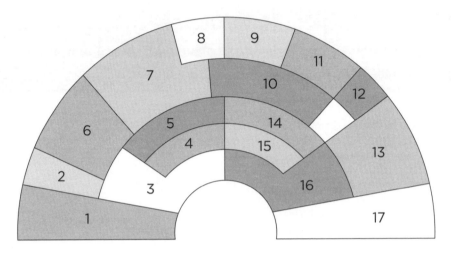

A symphony orchestra is dedicated to creating the most beautiful classical music – but it has some pretty strict rules when it comes to its seating plan. Can you remember where each instrument group is supposed to sit?

Our sincerest apologies to the piccolo players, saxophonists and conductors who were not included in this quiz.

a) First violin
b) Flute
c) Oboe
d) Tuba
e) Harp
f) Piano
g) Viola
h) Double bass

i) Cello
j) Trumpet
k) Trombone
l) Horn
m) Percussion
n) Bassoon
o) Clarinet
p) Second violin

HIDDEN COMPOSER

Solution on page 240.

The name of which composer is hidden in the sentence below? Discover it by joining words or parts of words together.

THE ORCHESTRA MEMBERS MET A NARRATOR WHO WAS GOING TO TAKE PART IN PROKOFIEV'S *PETER AND THE WOLF*.

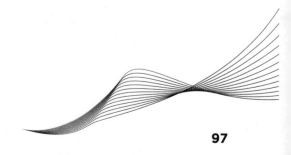

CODA: SING

Solution on page 240.

26	■	2	■	9	2	1	7	5	10	26	11	17
1 (S)	2 (I)	3 (N)	4 (G)	■	10	■	22	■	2	■	5	■
16	■	7	■	■	5	25	12	26	7	6	5	11
2	1	5	25	22	11	■	5	■	26	■	13	■
5	■	4	■	■	17	■	24	■	■	22	■	22
3	2	3	6	8	■	21	26	14	2	7	22	3
22	■	2	■	■	23	22	9	■	■	18	■	5
4	22	6	26	15	22	17	■	1	16	20	11	3
26	■	5	■	■	11	■	22	■	■	2	■	17
■	20	■	19	■	21	■	7	20	1	6	5	21
2	3	6	26	11	2	5	11	■	■	6	■	5
■	9	■	22	■	3	■	26	■	21	26	3	20
19	5	5	24	5	4	2	1	6	■	9	■	1

Each letter of the alphabet has been replaced by a number. Work out which number represents which letter to complete the crossword-style grid which has words reading across and down. You have the letters in the word SING to start you off.

Fill in the 1 to 26 grid with letters of the alphabet as you discover them.

1	2	3	4	5	6	7	8	9	10	11	12	13
14	15	16	17	18	19	20	21	22	23	24	25	26

When you have cracked the code, the letters 6, 8, 26, 21, 22, 4, 2, 7, 23, 24, 20, 6, 26 can be arranged to spell out a very famous opera with a three-word title.

6	8	26	21	22	4	2	7	23	24	20	6	26

COMPOSITION

Solution on page 241.

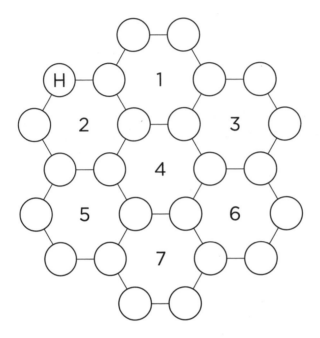

Fit the listed words into the frame, using the key letter as a starter. One letter goes in each circle, and words are written clockwise around a number. When all the words are in place, the addition of two letters will fill the grid and form the name of a composer.

DERAIL   HANDLE   NESTED

ENAMEL   HERBAL   RELISH

HIDDEN OPERA

Solution on page 242.

Which opera is hidden in the sentence below? Discover it by joining words or parts of words together.

WILL THE LADY PLAYING THE CELLO TELL OTHER PEOPLE WHAT HAS HAPPENED DURING THE ORCHESTRA REHEARSAL?

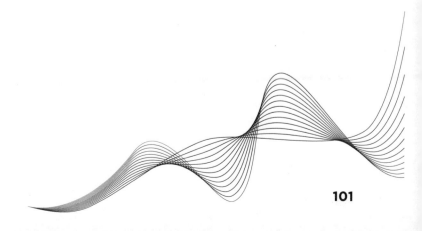

GUESS THE CLASSICAL PIECE... FOR PEOPLE WHO DON'T READ MUSIC

Solutions on page 242.

Test your knowledge of some of the greatest pieces of music ever written with our *incredibly* scientific quiz...

We wrote out some of the most famous pieces of classical music as vocalizations (that's doo-doo-doos to me and you). Can you match the doo-doo-deedle-dooing to the famous piece?

1.

**De de de de de de de
diddle-iddle-iddle-diddle
weeeeeeeeeee-AAAAAAAH**

**Diddle-iddle-iddle dee
dah dah DUM
dah dah DUM dah da DUM
dah da DAAAAAH**

a)   Gershwin: *Rhapsody in Blue*
b)   Rossini: *William Tell* Overture
c)   Wagner: 'Ride of the Valkyries' (from *Die Walküre*)
d)   John Williams: *Jaws* (score)

2.

**Ee ee ee ee ee
Ee ee ee ee ee
Ee ee ee ee ee**

a)   Beethoven: Symphony No. 5
b)   Gershwin: *Rhapsody in Blue*
c)   Herrmann: *Psycho* (score)
d)   Pachelbel: Canon in D

3.

Da da DUM, Da da DUM
da da DA da da Deee dah
da da DUM da
da da DUM
da da deedle dee da DAA

a) John Williams: *Star Wars* (score)
b) Brahms: Lullaby
c) John Williams: *Jaws* (score)
d) Saint-Saëns: *Danse Macabre*

4.

BAAAAAH
(diddly dum, diddly dum
diddly dum dum dum dum dum
dum dum dum etc)

Durr durr durr DUUUUU DUUUR
diddly DUUUUR DURRR
diddle DURRR DURRR diddly dum

a) John Williams: *Star Wars* (score)
b) John Williams: *Jaws* (score)
c) Rossini: *William Tell* Overture
d) Wagner: 'Ride of the Valkyries' (from *Die Walküre*)

5.

Baaaaah Baaaaah Baaaaah Baaaaah Baaaaah
Baaaaah Baaaaah (etc)

Deeee Deeee Deeee Deeee
Deeee Deeee Deeee Deeee (etc)

Laaaaa Laaaaa Laaaaa Laaaaa
Laaaaa Laaaaa Laaaaa (etc)

a) John Williams: *Jaws* (score)
b) Wagner: 'Ride of the Valkyries' (from *Die Walküre*)
c) Rossini: *William Tell* Overture
d) Pachelbel: Canon in D

6.

Dah Dah Dah DOOOM
Dah Dah Dah DOOOM

a)   Gershwin: *Rhapsody in Blue*
b)   John Williams: *Jaws* (score)
c)   Beethoven: Symphony No. 5
d)   Tchaikovsky: Dance of the Sugar Plum Fairy (from *The Nutcracker*)

7.

Plink plink plink plink plink plink plink plink plink plink etc.

a)   Gershwin: *Rhapsody in Blue*
b)   Saint-Saëns: *Danse Macabre*
c)   John Williams: *Star Wars* (score)
d)   Tchaikovsky: Dance of the Sugar Plum Fairy (from *The Nutcracker*)

8.

(Dum dada DA dada dum, dum dada DA dada dum, dum dada DA dada dum etc)

Dum dada DAAA daa, dum dada DAAA daa, dum dada DAAA daa, dum dada DAAAAAAAAAaaaa

a)   John Williams: *Star Wars* (score)
b)   Saint-Saëns: *Danse Macabre*
c)   Wagner: 'Ride of the Valkyries' (from *Die Walküre*)
d)   Tchaikovsky: Dance of the Sugar Plum Fairy (from *The Nutcracker*)

9.

Duh-duh
Duh-duh
Duh-duh
Duh-duh-duh-duh
Duh-duh-duh-duh-
Duh-duh-duh-duh
(di-di-di- di-di-di- di-di-di...etc)
deedle-dee deeeeeeeeeee

a) Herrmann: *Psycho* (score)
b) John Williams: *Jaws* (score)
c) Pachelbel: Canon in D
d) Beethoven: Symphony No. 5

10.

Diddle um diddle um
diddle DUM DUM DUM
Diddle um diddle um
diddle DUM DUM DUM
Diddle um diddle um
diddle DUM DUM DUM
Diddle DUUUUM,
diddle DUM DUM DUM

a) Rossini: *William Tell* Overture
b) Herrmann: *Psycho* (score)
c) Pachelbel: Canon in D
d) Beethoven: Symphony No. 5

PRESTO

Solution on page 243.

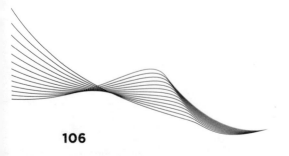

A classic quick crossword.

ACROSS

6 English conductor and a baby's toy (6)
7 'O mio babbino - - - -' (4)
9 Shostakovich soundtrack *The* - - - - - - (6)
10 Rhythm (5)
12 Performers in a show (4)
13 Opera by Bellini (5)
17 Number in an octet (5)
18 Conductor - - - - Glover (4)
21 Cellist - - - - - van der Heijden (5)
22 Grieg's home country (6)
24 Finishes, concludes (4)
25 Played with the feet on a piano (6)

DOWN

1 His music opened *2001: A Space Odyssey* (7)
2 Pitch (4)
3 Scott Joplin music (7)
4 Aria, 'Nessun - - - - -' (5)
5 French organist Charles-Marie - - - - - (5)
8 Instrument played with hammers (9)
11 Division of an opera (3)
14 Pianist and composer Ludovico - - - - - - - (7)
15 They are used in Latin American music (7)
16 Vivaldi was know as the - - - Priest (3)
19 English composer Lord - - - - - Webber (5)
20 Handel's 'The Arrival of the - - - - - of Sheba' (5)
23 Conductor André - - - - (4)

CODA: BEAT

Solution on page 244.

5		10		23	3	24	2	8	4	7	8	2
¹B	²E	³A	⁴T		1		9		5		2	
6		8		17	5	19	8	11	2	6	4	
4	7	11	12	4	6		7		3		4	
7		3			6		8			9		25
8	19	14	6	2		18	5	14	22	19	24	3
3		5			1	5	16			7		14
4	14	5	5	21	2	14		26	5	13	2	8
2		6			20		6			13		3
	15		4		7		4	17	21	7	6	4
1	3	11	19	2	4	4	2			25		7
	7		1		25		2		12	3	24	5
2	24	6	2	20	12	2	14	2		24		8

Each letter of the alphabet has been replaced by a number. Work out which number represents which letter to complete the crossword-style grid which has words reading across and down. You have the letters in the word BEAT to start you off.

Fill in the 1 to 26 grid with letters of the alphabet as you discover them.

1	2	3	4	5	6	7	8	9	10	11	12	13
14	15	16	17	18	19	20	21	22	23	24	25	26

When you have cracked the code, the letters 25, 5, 8, 26, 19, 25, 4, 5, 14 can be arranged to spell out a word with a link to the starter word.

25	5	8	26	19	25	4	5	14

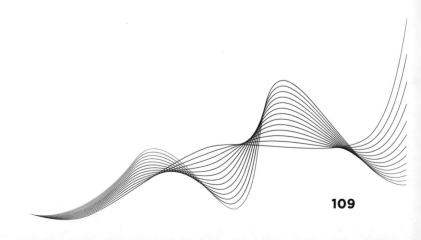

COMPOSITION

Solution on page 245.

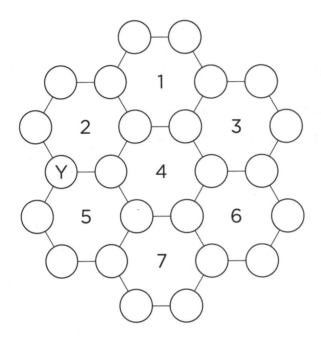

Fit the listed words into the frame, using the key letter as a starter. One letter goes in each circle, and words are written clockwise around a number. When all the words are in place, the addition of two letters will fill the grid and form the name of a composer.

HERESY	PERUSE	SUMMER
MISUSE	SIZZLE	SURVEY

OPERA OR CHEESE?

Solutions on page 246.

Think you know your opera from your cheese? It's time to put your knowledge to the test. Decide if each word is the name of an opera or a type of cheese.

1	Cavalleria rusticana	11	Saga
2	Époisses de Bourgogne	12	Scamorza
3	Bear Hill	13	Il Re Pastore
4	Blue Monday	14	Dalibor
5	Casu Marzu	15	Abbaye de Belloc
6	Platée	16	Remoudou
7	Anari	17	Fidelio
8	La Dame Blanche	18	La Périchole
9	Passendale	19	Fiore Sardo
10	The Nose	20	Västerbottensost

CODA: LUTE

Solution on page 247.

4		9		10	1	10	21	10	9	3	4	23
¹L	²U	³T	⁴E		10		4		4		25	
5		10			21	2	1	1	4	3	11	7
6	2	11	8	19	4		11		18		3	
2		23			1		4			8		16
4	25	8	4	1		5	22	4	23	10	1	1
7		10			4	12	4			16		10
8	5	9	3	2	20	4		17	23	4	4	3
4		4			26		23			3		3
	15		3		10		10	7	7	4	25	4
23	4	14	4	8	3	4	24			23		23
	23		10		19		10		14	11	22	4
8	5	2	23	3	13	10	23	24		10		24

Each letter of the alphabet has been replaced by a number. Work out which number represents which letter to complete the crossword-style grid which has words reading across and down. You have the letters in the word LUTE to start you off.

Fill in the 1 to 26 grid with letters of the alphabet as you discover them.

1	2	3	4	5	6	7	8	9	10	11	12	13
14	15	16	17	18	19	20	21	22	23	24	25	26

When you have cracked the code, the letters 8, 1, 10, 22, 11, 8, 19, 5, 23, 24 can be arranged to spell out another instrument.

8	1	10	22	11	8	19	5	23	24

RING CYCLE

Solution on page 248.

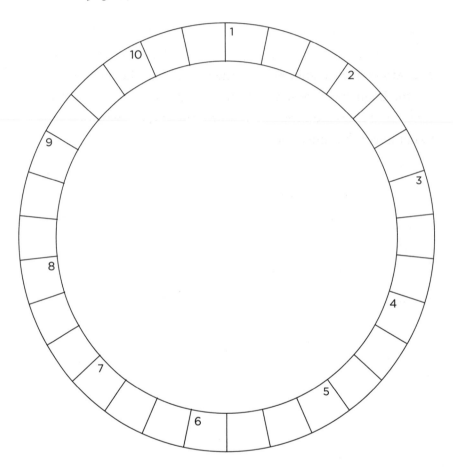

Solve the clues below, which are in no particular order, and slot the five-letter answers into their correct places in the ring. The last two letters of each answer form the first two of the next. Answer 1 is the English composer. Answer 5 also has a musical link. The remaining clues are general in nature, and there is only one way to complete the ring cycle.

CLUES
Flat
Piece of dining room furniture
Wear away
English composer from Worcester
Stadium, large performance space
His first major work was not performed until almost 80 years after his death
Evidence you were elsewhere when a crime was committed
Mouth of a river
Relating to the nose
Colourless liquid used as an anaesthetic

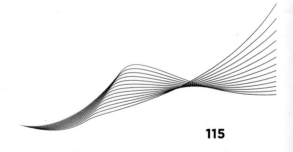

HIDDEN MUSIC

Solution on page 248.

The name of a form of choral works is hidden in the sentence below. Discover it by joining words or parts of words together.

DESPITE TECHNICAL EXCELLENCE AND A VOICE THAT GLIDES THROUGH THE OCTAVES, PERSONALITY-WISE THE PERFORMANCE OF THE SOPRANO LACKED CONVICTION.

SECTION 2: ACCELERANDO

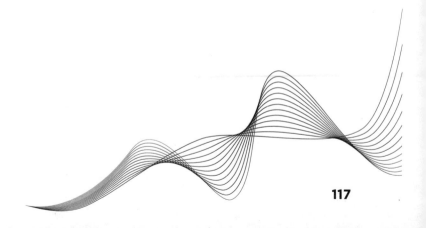

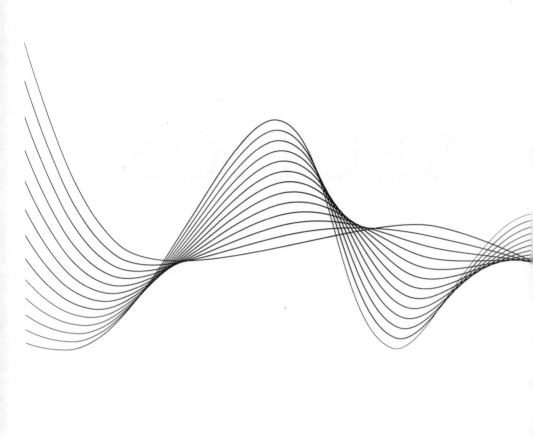

QUESTIONS
SECTION THREE

MOLTO VIVACE

(Italian: 'very lively' or 'at a very quick speed'.)
Even the classical music experts among
you will be challenged by the puzzles
in this section.

CAN YOU MATCH THE COMPOSER TO THEIR COUNTRY OF BIRTH?

Solutions on page 252–3.

Many composers travelled around the world, seeking work and inspiration. But do you know where they were actually born?

1.
Antonio Vivaldi

a) Portugal
b) France
c) Spain
d) Italy

2.
Joaquín Rodrigo

a) Portugal
b) Chile
c) Mexico
d) Spain

3.
Béla Bartók

a) Czech Republic
b) Russia
c) Bulgaria
d) Hungary

4.
Claude Debussy

a) France
b) Switzerland
c) America
d) England

5.
Frédéric Chopin

a) France
b) England
c) Poland
d) Switzerland

6.
Franz Liszt

a) Czech Republic
b) Germany
c) Russia
d) Hungary

7.
John Williams

a) United States
b) England
c) Italy
d) France

8.
Antonín Dvořák

a) Russia
b) Finland
c) Czech Republic
d) Hungary

9.
George Gershwin

a) Czech Republic
b) Germany
c) United States
d) Russia

10.
Sergei Rachmaninov

a) Ukraine
b) Germany
c) Hungary
d) Russia

11.
Jean Sibelius

a) Czech Republic
b) Finland
c) Russia
d) Poland

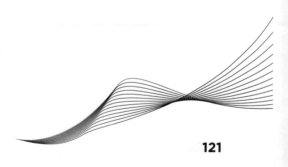

12.
Edward Elgar

a) America
b) Holland
c) England
d) Germany

13.
Frederick Delius

a) Germany
b) America
c) England
d) France

14.
Wolfgang Amadeus Mozart

a) Russia
b) Poland
c) Austria
d) Germany

15.
Sergei Prokofiev

a) Ukraine
b) Poland
c) Hungary
d) Russia

16.
Ennio Morricone

a) Italy
b) Spain
c) America
d) Malta

17.
Pyotr Tchaikovsky

a) Ukraine
b) Russia
c) Poland
d) Finland

18.
George Frideric Handel

a) Poland
b) Germany
c) Austria
d) England

19.
Edvard Grieg

a) Sweden
b) Poland
c) Finland
d) Norway

20.
Ludwig van Beethoven

a) Germany
b) Ukraine
c) Switzerland
d) Austria

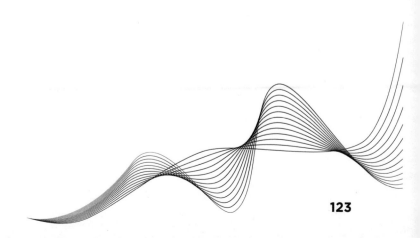

ENIGMA VARIATIONS

Solution on page 254.

A cryptic crossword.

ACROSS

7   Bliss Symphony not in black and white (6)
9   Spare nothing whatsoever in these musical works (6)
10 No din I'm due to make, getting even quieter (10)
11 Leaves Oslo, alone (4)
12 Strikes different beast (5)
13 Organs, for example, of significant groups of directors (9)
16 Trembles at eighth notes (7)
21 Voice found at control (9)
22 Plead again for a musical lever (5)
24 Air a new song (4)
25 Artist Gus and I are like Segovia and Rodrigo (10)
26 Disunited unions now of one voice (6)
27 Underwear ship composer (6)

DOWN

1   Posters from a different section (7)
2   East city so disrupted by association (7)
3   Tutor reinterprets Schubert quintet (5)
4   Bedtime drink, we hear, for Gilbert & Sullivan character (4)
5   She aims to conduct oratorio (7)
6   Ad Bella produced for piano piece (7)
8   A riot in the middle of jam at music school (13)
14 Restaurant counters musical divisions (4)
15 Sounds like a root in the wind department (4)
17 Signora gets flustered aiming for the high notes (7)
18 Tarsus's loss was Vienna's gain (7)
19 Fresh article about concert popularized by Liszt (7)
20 Maigret discovers 20th-century music (7)
23 We see Sam balancing carefully in Latin routine (5)
25 Wagon gingerly making an appearance to the sound of a bell (4)

PRESTO

Solution on page 254.

A classic quick crossword.

ACROSS

6   High pitched (6)
7   Large valved instrument (4)
9   Romanian soprano - - - - - - Gheorghiu (6)
10 American composer - - - - - Copland (5)
12 '- - - - of the Valkyries' (4)
13 Cellist - - - - - Kanneh-Mason (5)
17 Manner, way of playing (5)
18 Stravinsky's The - - - - of Spring (4)
21 Christmas song (5)
22 Mozart concerto, used in film - - - - - - Madigan (6)
24 Improvised jazz singing (4)
25 'The Knightsbridge March' by Eric - - - - - - (6)

DOWN

1   Violinist Nigel (7)
2   The Danube according to Johann Strauss II (4)
3   Dvořák opera including 'Song to the Moon' (7)
4   Composer and conductor of film music John - - - - - (5)
5   Lang Lang's instrument (5)
8   His Canon and Gigue has made him famous (9)
11 Gershwin brother (3)
14 Nationality of Pavarotti (7)
15 This produces a tremulous effect (7)
16 Abbreviation for the New York Metropolitan Opera (3)
19 Ascending or descending range of notes (5)
20 Instrument such as the cornet (5)
23 Baroque stringed instrument (4)

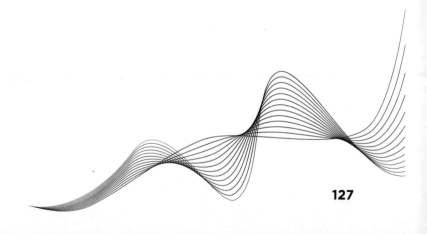

OCTET

Solution on page 255.

Solve the clues below to find the eight-letter answers. The first letter of the answer goes in the numbered square, and the answer can go clockwise or anticlockwise. We tell you if it is (C) clockwise or (A) anticlockwise.

CLUES

1   Italian composer famous for his Adagio in G Minor, which was, in fact, written by someone else (C)
2   New York thoroughfare famous for its theatres (A)
3   Musical work such as Handel's *Messiah* (A)
4   *The - - - - - - - -* by Stravinsky had its premiere in Paris in 1910 (A)
5   Famous aria sung by the title character in Bizet's *Carmen* (A)
6   Tchaikovsky ballet (4,4) (A)
7   Renowned for his Unfinished Symphony, which he inexplicably abandoned six years before his death (A)
8   Italian violinist of the late 18th and early 19th century (C)
9   Low male voice (A)
10 Practise for a performance (C)
11 Allegri's psalm appealing for mercy (C)
12 Theme from the movie *The Deer Hunter* (A)
13 Earlier name for radio (C)
14 Smallest interval in classical European music (C)
15 Waltzes made famous by Strauss (A)
16 Part of a longer musical work (C)
17 Highly skilled performer (A)
18 Nationality of Aaron Copland (A)
19 Surname of brothers George and Ira (A)
20 Describes all a writer's works (A)
21 Creator of musical pieces (A)
22 Decade famous for its lively dance, the charleston (A)
23 Tape cartridge used for playing music (C)
24 Appreciation by clapping (C)
25 Performers who perform alone (C)
26 Test for suitability for a role or for performance (A)
27 Groups of musicians of four (C)
28 Words that go with a piece of music (C)

CAN YOU COMPLETE THE FAMOUS QUOTE FROM EACH COMPOSER?

Solutions on page 256.

We've gathered some of our favourite quotes from the great composers, but can you fill in the blanks?

1.
Claude Debussy:
'Works of _____ make rules; rules do not make works of _____.'

a) music
b) art
c) brilliance
d) God

2.
Leonard Bernstein:
'To achieve great things, two things are needed; a plan, and not quite enough _____.'

a) time
b) people
c) money
d) sleep

3.
Béla Bartók:
'Competitions are for _____, not artists.'

a) normal people
b) horses
c) sportsmen
d) dogs

4.
Igor Stravinsky:
'Lesser artists borrow, great artists _____.'

a) steal
b) create
c) dream
d) thrive

5.
Edward Elgar:
'I always said _____ was against art and I still believe it.'

a) God
b) the world
c) Stravinsky
d) society

6.
Johannes Brahms:
'Without _____, inspiration is a mere reed shaken in the wind.'

a) refinement
b) craftsmanship
c) money
d) motivation

7.

Joseph Haydn:

'There was no one near to _____ me, so I was forced to become original.'

a)   distract
b)   inspire
c)   confuse
d)   influence

8.

J S Bach:

'I was obliged to be _____. Whoever is equally _____ will succeed equally well.'

a)   happy
b)   inspired
c)   industrious
d)   determined

9.

Erik Satie:

'The musician is perhaps the most modest of animals, but he is also the _____.'

a)   proudest
b)   saddest
c)   most complicated
d)   most selfish

10.

Robert Schumann:

'To send light into the darkness of men's hearts – such is the _____ of the artist.'

a)   will
b)   duty
c)   want
d)   obligation

11.

Dmitri Shostakovich:

'A creative artist works on his next composition because he was not _____ with his previous one.'

a)   satisfied
b)   impressed
c)   content
d)   amused

12.

John Cage:

'I can't understand why people are _____ of new ideas. I'm _____ of the old ones.'

a)   wary
b)   in awe
c)   frightened
d)   anxious

13.

Giacomo Puccini:

'_____ is an awakening, a quickening of all man's faculties, and it is manifested in all high artistic achievements.'

a)   Art
b)   Inspiration
c)   Money
d)   Music

14.

Richard Wagner:

'_____ creates reality.'

a)   Music
b)   Imagination
c)   Opera
d)   Art

METRONOME

Solution on page 257.

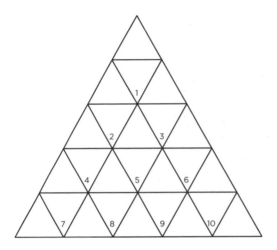

Each answer contains four letters. The first letter goes in a numbered triangle, the second letter directly above it, the third letter to the right and the fourth to the left.

CLUES

1   Gershwin's Rhapsody colour.
2   Ibsen's - - - - *Gynt* Suites.
3   Patriotic song, '- - - - Britannia!'
4   London summer concert at the Albert Hall.
5   The good guy in movies.
6   Notation indicating that notes are played without separation.
7   Final word of a hymn.
8   Edward MacDowell composition 'To a Wild - - - -'.
9   Music, painting and sculpture.
10 Famous contralto Dame Clara - - - -.

SESTET

Solution on page 257.

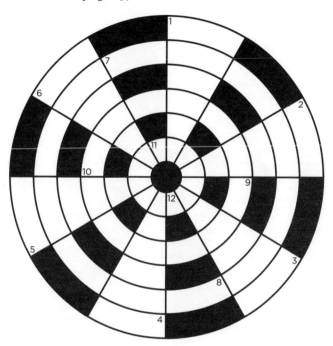

All answers have six letters. 1 to 6 start in the outer circle
and are written toward the centre. 7 to 12 go around the rings
in a clockwise direction.

CLUES

1   Orchestral stringed instrument played by Clue 7.
2   Songs where groups join in separately but in turn.
3   Composer of *Belshazzar's Feast*.
4   In 1982, Marvin Hamlisch composed the score to the movie *Sophie's* - - - - - -.
5   Dvořák and Smetana had close links with this city, now capital of the
     Czech Republic.
6   Concert Hall in Kensington, west London, named after a Prince Consort.
7   First name of the winner of the Young Musician of the Year 2004, aged 16.
8   Beethoven's 9th is also called the - - - - - - Symphony.
9   Bach's famous Air on a G - - - - - -.
10   Capital city, and the surname of the composer of 'White Christmas'.
11   Singers singing as one, with no harmonies.
12   Go over a phrase or verse more than once.

CAN YOU NAME ALL THESE CLEFS?

Solution on page 258.

1.

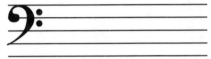

a) Treble
b) Bass
c) Tenor
d) Alto

2.

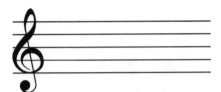

a) Alto
b) Tenor
c) Bass
d) Treble

3.

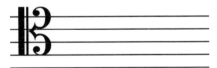

a) Alto
b) Bass
c) Baritone
d) Tenor

4.

a) Bass
b) Alto
c) Tenor
d) Baritone

5.

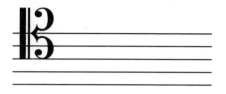

a) Baritone
b) French violin
c) Tenor
d) Alto

8.

a) Alto
b) Soprano
c) Tenor
d) Baritone

6.

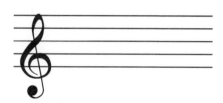

a) Soprano
b) Alto
c) French violin
d) Treble

9.

a) Treble
b) Piccolo
c) French violin
d) Octave

7.

a) Percussion
b) Bass
c) Double bass
d) Baritone

10.

a) Baritone
b) Tenor
c) Bass
d) Subbass

CAN YOU TRANSLATE THESE BASIC ITALIAN MUSICAL TERMS?

Solutions on page 258.

Does *allegro* mean you should play it fast, or is it a brass technique? This quiz will test your prowess with those familiar (and not so familiar) musical terms.

1.
Andante

a)   A moderately fast piece of music
b)   A fast piece of music
c)   A graceful piece of music

2.
Fermata

a)   Loudly
b)   Stop
c)   A prolonged note

3.
Tremolo

a)   In a hesitant, frightened manner
b)   A rapid back and forth movement on the same note
c)   In an excited manner

4.
Cantabile

a)   In a singable fashion
b)   Slowly
c)   With laughter

5.
Ritardando

a)   Slow down abruptly
b)   Speed up gradually
c)   Slow down gradually

6.
Diminuendo

a)   Gradually get quieter
b)   Play with sudden and marked emphasis
c)   A musical ornament

7.
Cadenza

a) A prolonged note
b) A virtuoso solo passage
c) A musical suite, usually for solo instrument

8.
Da Capo

a) From the cadenza
b) From the 'capo' sign
c) From the beginning

9.
Basso continuo

a) A very low bass singer
b) A double bass
c) Figured bass

10.
Giocoso

a) Mournfully
b) Playfully
c) Curiously

11.
Ostinato

a) A musical phrase which persistently repeats
b) Played stubbornly
c) Played firmly, with force

12.
Presto

a) Jauntily
b) Suddenly loud
c) In a quick tempo

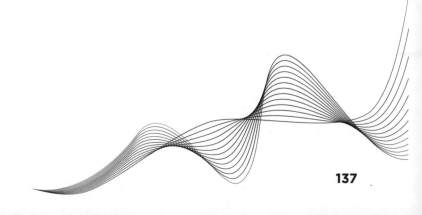

TEST YOUR KNOWLEDGE OF MUSIC NOTATION

Solutions on page 259.

From plainsong to jianpu, challenge your musical notation expertise with this quiz.

1.
When was the earliest form of music notation written?

a) 1945
b) 1782
c) *c.*2000 BC
d) *c.*1450

2.
What was early plainsong notation called?

a) Neumes
b) Names
c) Nodes
d) Nats

3.
This is called a...

a) Punctum
b) Clivis
c) Virga
d) Bipunctum

4.
How many lines are on a modern standard single stave?

a) 5
b) 4
c) 2
d) 1

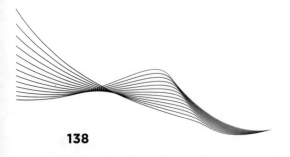

5.

These are called...

a) Incidentals
b) Intentionals
c) Accidentals
d) Coincidentals

6.

What is this symbol called?

a) Tremolo
b) Glissando
c) Trattenuto
d) It does not exist

7.

This symbol means that you must...

a) Accent this note
b) Play this note pizzicato
c) Up bow this note
d) Pause on this note

8.

What is this symbol?

a) An accent
b) It does not exist
c) Half a hashtag
d) A demisharp

9.
What is this symbol?

a) Quasi-common split time
b) Common alla breve
c) It does not exist
d) Demi breve time

10.
What is a sesquiflat?

a) A three-quarter-tone flat
b) A grace note/ornament
c) It does not exist
d) A Baroque instrument

11.
A British demisemihemidemisemi-quaver is an American...

a) Hundred twenty-eight note
b) Two hundred fifty-sixth note
c) Three hundred seventy-fourth note
d) Octuple whole note

12.
Fill in the gaps: do re mi _ _ _ _ do.

a) La ti sol fa
b) Ti la sol fa
c) Sol fa ti la
d) Fa sol la ti

13.

If d is sol, what number is it in Chinese
numbered notation (jianpu)?

a)   2
b)   4
c)   7
d)   5

14.

Also in jianpu, which of the following is
a quaver/eighth note?

a)   b)   c)   d)

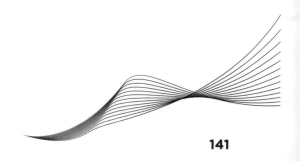

ENIGMA VARIATIONS

Solution on page 260.

A cryptic crossword.

ACROSS

7 Vehicle before us, ring a great tenor (6)

9 Change of events for cellist Isserlis (6)

10 16th-century composer ashen with contorted strain (10)

11 Lots of arrangements of Sullivan's chord (4)

12 In 24 hours the Spanish hold back opening of a new show (5)

13 Outpouring of feelings as men ail, too (9)

16 Out somehow, Wagner's cycle is on the road (7)

21 Self-employed musician plays for nothing, clean in appearance (9)

22 Fruit for tenor Peter? (5)

24 At Brigg or Scarborough it sounds reasonable (4)

25 Months to record the speed and the livin' is easy (10)

26 After changing I led us to reveal a composer (6)

27 My boy at a piece of classical music? (6)

DOWN

1 Nocturnal mammal lands in care providing evening entertainment (7)

2 Real fun arranged? A requiem more in keeping (7)

3 Strange effort loses a symbol that stands for it (5)

4 Borodin landscape can be found, as I argued from the start (4)

5 Sounds as if stocky Australian produced music (7)

6 Reps in a flap naming Eastern market (7)

8 Wise partner playing all the right notes but not necessarily in the right order (4,9)

14 Fish responsible for keeping a piano up to pitch, we hear (4)

15 Fish a sign to play it again (4)

17 Had a tantrum, produced a new piece of music (7)

18 Give up where everyone else joins in (7)

19 Adapting words to music like the sinking of the sun (7)

20 Advance someone in their career path while trying to sell the concert (7)

23 A poor serve taking place in a song (5)

25 Window to see conductor's cummerbund (4)

HEXACHORDS

Solution on page 261.

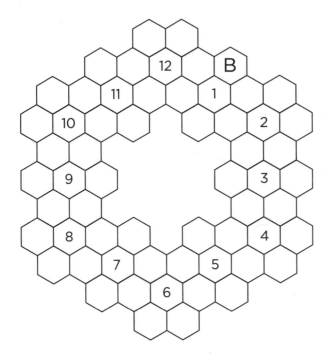

All answers have six letters and fit into the grid reading in a clockwise direction. We give you the starting point for the answer to Clue 1, but after that you have to work out in which hexagonal cell the answer begins.

CLUES

1 20th-century American composer Samuel - - - - - -.
2 Country that is the home of the samba.
3 The - - - - - - bass is a very large stringed instrument.
4 Tune, air.
5 High-pitched voice.
6 Set of successive radio or TV programmes that link.
7 Not flats!
8 Individual pieces in a collection of recorded music.
9 Small harpsichord.
10 Elgar's - - - - - - *Variations*.
11 Time of year when a theatre will put on a number of shows or concerts.
12 Fame, notoriety.

METRONOME

Solution on page 261.

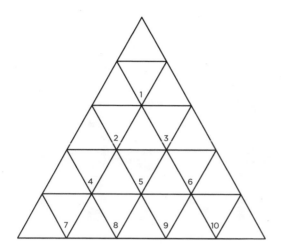

Each answer contains four letters. The first letter goes in a numbered triangle, the second letter directly above it, the third letter to the right and the fourth to the left..

CLUES
1 Puccini opera, *The - - - - of the West*.
2 Applaud to show appreciation.
3 'One Fine Day', for example.
4 Begin to perform a run of shows in a theatre.
5 'Remember me, but ah! forget my - - - -'.
6 Cadence or swing.
7 Rimsky-Korsakov opera *The - - - - Maiden*.
8 Short note, but not a musical one!
9 Piece included in the concert programme.
10 Unaccompanied singing.

OCTET

Solution on page 262.

Solve the clues below to find the eight-letter answers. The first letter of the answer goes in the numbered square, and the answer can go clockwise or anticlockwise. We tell you if it is (C) clockwise or (A) anticlockwise.

CLUES

1. Gershwin's masterpiece - - - - - - - - *in Blue* (A)
2. 1940 Disney movie, with music by Stravinsky, Ponchielli and Mussorgsky, among others (C)
3. A practical teaching session (A)
4. First name of pianist/composer Einaudi (C)
5. A brief summary of the plot of a musical or opera (A)
6. Woodwind instrument (C)
7. Volume of religious songs (4,4) (A)
8. Jacqueline du Pre recorded Elgar's Cello - - - - - - - -, conducted by John Barbirolli, in the mid-1960s (C)
9. Someone who adapts an original work for a particular performance (C)
10. The notes of a chord played separately, in sequence (C)
11. Introductory pieces of music; one of them might precede a fugue or opera (C)
12. John Williams wrote the score for - - - - - - - - *Park*, directed by Steven Spielberg (C)
13. This word describes the Magpie in Rossini's opera (A)
14. Released a record, but not for the first time (A)
15. A ballerina (A)
16. Nationality of composer Arvo Pärt (C)
17. A pianist, a cellist, or a violinist, for example (A)
18. These double-reed instruments date from the 17th century (A)
19. Puccini opera, which features 'Nessun Dorma' (A)
20. Notes producing a melancholy effect (5,3) (C)
21. Mussorgsky's - - - - - - - - *at an Exhibition* (A)
22. Improvised (2,6) (A)
23. Operetta featuring John Wellington Wells, *The* - - - - - - - - (A)
24. Keyboard player, often in a church (A)
25. Rimsky-Korsakov's The Young Prince and the Young - - - - - - - - from *Scheherazade* (A)
26. Wandering medieval musician (C)
27. Conductor, Sir John Eliot - - - - - - - - (C)
28. Musical instrument often used in schools (A)

ENIGMA VARIATIONS

Solution on page 262.

A cryptic crossword.

ACROSS

7   Butcher, we hear on Delius's ride (6)
9   I go with Ada at a leisurely pace (6)
10 Betrothal at gig (10)
11 Team drum (4)
12 Investigate instrumental piece (5)
13 The one Bev discovered was a genius (9)
16 Musical benefactors handed out no parts (7)
21 Bad-tempered strings in Tell's overture (9)
22 Use this to direct the orchestra from the *boulangerie*? (5)
24 Austen heroine is the first name on the clarinet (4)
25 I do dodgier alterations to aboriginal instrument (10)
26 Gems, of Bizet's fishers? (6)
27 Consort or concert hall? (6)

DOWN

1   Heavenly works (7)
2   After six and five, somehow dial the red priest (7)
3   Musical manuscript on the bed? (5)
4   Performers set in stone (4)
5   Tubas so on trend revealing source of low sound (7)
6   Cheating violinist? (7)
8   Lehár's jolly spider (3,5,5)
14 Sound of discordant note (4)
15 Soothing balm from the Agnus Dei (4)
17 Elephant call in the brass section (7)
18 Sounds like a step from Gershwin's dog walker (7)
19 This was hammered and led to rib Mama cracked (7)
20 Joseph's coat boasted many influences (7)
23 Elgar became something quite magnificent (5)
25 Compact at one time and of use to a jockey (4)

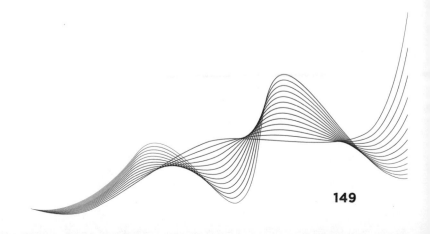

HOW WELL DO YOU KNOW THE FIRST NAMES OF THE GREAT COMPOSERS?

Solutions on page 263.

Everyone knows the great composers by their surnames – but what about their first names?

1.
Beethoven

a)   Heinrich von
b)   Lester von
c)   Aldrich van
d)   Ludwig van

2.
Smetana

a)   Bedrich
b)   Heinrich
c)   Gunter van
d)   Godrich

3.
Tchaikovsky

a)   Nikolai
b)   Vladimir
c)   Sergei
d)   Pyotr

4.
Glass

a)   William
b)   Edward
c)   Nigel
d)   Philip

5.
Liszt

a)   Franz
b)   Johannes
c)   Jean
d)   Frederic

6.
Donizetti

a)   Gioachino
b)   Guido
c)   Gaetano
d)   Francesco

7.
Corelli

a)   Francesco
b)   Arcangelo
c)   Ludovico
d)   Tomaso

8.
Brahms

a)   Richard
b)   Claude
c)   Franz
d)   Johannes

9.
Debussy

a)   Claude
b)   Jean
c)   Leo
d)   Maurice

10.
Sibelius

a)   Manuel
b)   Hector
c)   Jean
d)   Johannes

SESTET

Solution on page 263.

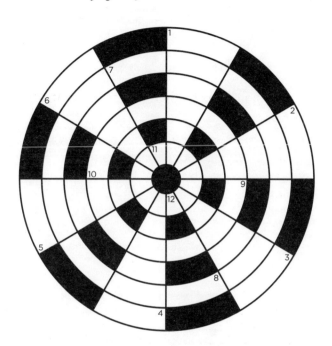

All answers have six letters. 1 to 6 start in the outer circle and are written toward the centre. 7 to 12 go around the rings in a clockwise direction.

CLUES

1. Plucked stringed instrument originally from Austria and Bavaria.
2. Orchestra conductor with the first name of John, famous for his adaptation of Hollywood musicals.
3. Wagnerian opera *Tristan and* - - - - - -.
4. First name of violinist Menuhin.
5. The aria 'When I am laid in earth' is known as Dido's - - - - - -.
6. Travelled widely performing.
7. Notes that are twice the length of crotchets.
8. In a smooth and flowing manner.
9. Debussy's first name.
10. German composer born in 1833 whose works included four symphonies and four concertos.
11. Royal title of Tamino in *The Magic Flute*.
12. Naturally talented.

THE HARDEST EVER MOZART QUIZ

Solutions on page 264.

Try your hand at this quiz about the brilliant man behind some of the greatest music ever written.

1.
What was the name Mozart was baptized under?

a) Wolfgang Leopold Amadeus Mozart
b) Johannes Chrysostomus Wolfgangus Theophilus Mozart
c) Leopold Wolfgang Mozart
d) Wolfgang Amadeus Mozart

2.
What was the nickname of his older sister, Maria Anna?

a) Annie
b) Nannerl
c) Nanni
d) Marianne

3.
How old was Mozart when he wrote his first symphony?

a) Eight
b) Six
c) Seven
d) Five

4.
Which of these is not a character in Mozart's opera Idomeneo?

a) Ilia
b) Idamante
c) Orestes
d) Elettra

5.
How many piano concertos did Mozart write?

a) 46
b) 23
c) 35
d) 51

6.

What was the name of the librettist with whom Mozart worked for the opera Die Entführung aus dem Serail?

a) Lorenzo da Ponte
b) Gottlieb Stephanie
c) Vittorio Amedeo Cigna-Santi
d) Emanuel Schikaneder

7.

What was the name of the woman with whom Mozart fell in love in the 1770s, but didn't marry? (He actually married her sister!)

a) Josepha Weber
b) Sophie Weber
c) Aloysia Weber
d) Constanze Weber

8.

What is Papageno's job in the opera The Magic Flute?

a) Birdcatcher
b) Butler
c) Messenger
d) Singer

9.

For which of these instruments did Mozart write a concerto?

a) Banjo
b) Ondes Martenot
c) Triangle
d) Glass harmonica

HOW WELL DO YOU KNOW YOUR MUSICAL NICKNAMES?

Solution on page 265.

Are these nicknames for pieces of classical music, or completely random words? Handy hint: listen to the music for each question and see if you think it suits the nickname.

1.
'Raindrop' is...

a) the nickname for a Chopin piano prelude.
b) a completely random word.

2.
'Envelope' is...

a) the nickname for Corelli's Concerto Grosso No. 7 in D.
b) a completely random word.

3.
'Toy' is...

a) the nickname for Mozart's Cassation in G major.
b) a completely random word.

4.
'London' is...

a) the nickname for Haydn's Symphony No. 104.
b) a completely random word.

5.
'Emperor' is...

a) the nickname for Beethoven's Piano Concerto No. 5.
b) a completely random word.

6.
'Milan' is...

a) the nickname for Finzi's Romance in E flat major.
b) a completely random word.

7.
'Nordic' is...

a)   the nickname for Hanson's
     Symphony No. 1.
b)   a completely random word.

8.
'Sunrise' is...

a)   the nickname for Saint-Saëns's
     Symphony No. 2.
b)   a completely random word.

9.
'State' is...

a)   the nickname for Bernstein's
     Divertimento for Orchestra.
b)   a completely random word.

10.
'Trout' is...

a)   the nickname for Schubert's Piano
     Quintet.
b)   a completely random word.

11.
'Ship' is...

a)   the nickname for Marcello's Oboe
     Concerto in D minor.
b)   a completely random word.

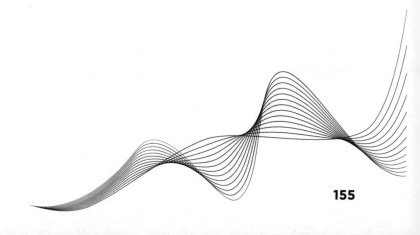

12.
'Stroll' is...

a)   the nickname for Brahms's Symphony No. 4.
b)   a completely random word.

13.
'Mountain' is...

a)   the nickname for Tchaikovsky's Piano Concerto No. 1.
b)   a completely random word.

14.
'Concord' is...

a)   the nickname for Ives's Piano Sonata No. 2.
b)   a completely random word.

15.
'Cow' is...

a)   the nickname for Danzi's Wind Quintet op. 56, No. 1.
b)   a completely random word.

16.
'Ocean' is...

a)   the nickname for Rubinstein's Symphony No. 2.
b)   a completely random word.

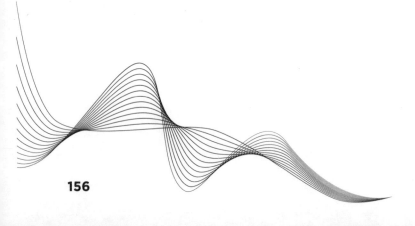

17.
'Box' is...

a) the nickname for Philip Glass's String Quartet No. 5.
b) a completely random word.

18.
'Butterfly' is...

a) the nickname for Chopin's Étude op. 25, No. 9.
b) a completely random word.

19.
'Surprise' is...

a) the nickname for Haydn's Symphony No. 94.
b) a completely random word.

20.
'Jupiter' is...

a) the nickname for Holst's Suite op. 32, No. 4.
b) a completely random word.

QUIZ CROSSWORD

Solution on page 266.

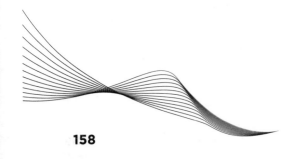

A crossword with a twist. Work out the answer to each question in order to fill the grid.

ACROSS

7 Which piece of musical theatre has music adapted from pieces composed by Borodin? (6)

9 What are the words of a song also called? (6)

10 Which devices mark the time of a piece by giving a regular click? (10)

11 Was Beethoven mute or deaf? (4)

12 Which nickname is given to Haydn's Symphony No. 101? (5)

13 What is another name for a cinema fan? (9)

15 Which word means to represent dramatically in a play or opera? (7)

20 Who was the Egyptian heroine in Handel's *Giulio Cesare*? (9)

21 Which part of a song is sung before the refrain? (5)

23 Which William is the subject of a famous overture by Rossini? (4)

24 Which metal pipe has six holes, which when blown produce different notes? (3,7)

25 How is an author or creator also known? (6)

26 Which dance of French origin has music in triple time? (6)

DOWN

1 Which ballet, with music by Adolphe Adam, premiered in Paris in 1841? (7)

2 In which country was Dvořák's String Quartet in F, op. 96, composed? (7)

3 What does the audience traditionally do during Handel's Hallelujah Chorus? (5)

4 How is Prokofiev's Symphony No. 1 in D also known? (9)

5 Which term is applied to an exceptionally talented child, such as Mozart? (7)

6 What are the eight notes in a scale called? (7)

8 Which US fantasy drama series has music by Ramin Djawadi? (4,2,7)

14 Which word completes the music by Ketèlbey, *In a - - - - - - - - - Garden*? (9)

16 Which musical term means 'with a brisk tempo'? (7)

17 In Holst's *The Planets*, what is Jupiter the bringer of? (7)

18 What completes the name of one of Vivaldi's most famous works, *The Four - - - - - - -*? (7)

19 What name is given to a book of songs from the Old Testament of the Bible? (7)

22 What is a set of attuned bells called? (5)

HEXACHORDS

Solution on page 266.

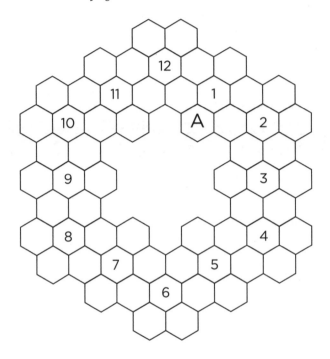

All answers have six letters and fit into the grid reading in a clockwise direction. We give you the starting point for the answer to Clue 1, but after that you have to work out in which hexagonal cell the answer begins.

CLUES

1   First name of English conductor Davis.
2   Cellist, Julian Lloyd - - - - - -.
3   Festive times with music and dancing.
4   Advertised, publicized on posters.
5   First name of trumpeter Ms Balsom.
6   King of the fairies in *A Midsummer Night's Dream*.
7   Composer Berlioz's first name.
8   Home of serenading gondoliers.
9   A waltz that might have lasted only 60 seconds!
10   A drum, maybe found in the kitchen.
11   Mouse which conducted the orchestra in *Fantasia*.
12   *Enigma Variation* in which Elgar paid tribute to his friend A J Jaeger.

METRONOME

Solution on page 267.

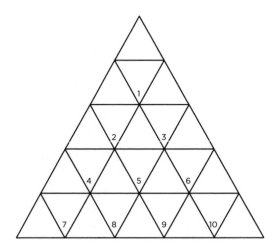

Each answer contains FOUR letters. The first letter goes in a numbered triangle, the second letter directly above it, the third letter to the right and the fourth to the left.

CLUES

1   Movie about a pig that featured music by Saint-Saëns.
2   Used in the mouthpiece of a clarinet.
3   Woodwind instrument.
4   Vaughan Williams composition *On Wenlock* - - - -.
5   Composer of the operas *Wozzeck* and *Lulu*.
6   Othello, the - - - - of Venice.
7   South American country linked with panpipe music.
8   Borodin's operatic prince.
9   The Jacques Loussier - - - -.
10 Mozart opera - - - - *Fan Tutte*.

OCTET

Solution on page 267.

Solve the clues below to find the eight-letter answers. The first letter of the answer goes in the numbered square, and the answer can go clockwise or anticlockwise. We tell you if it is (C) clockwise or (A) anticlockwise.

CLUES

1   Rodrigo's *Concierto de - - - - - - - -* was inspired by a beautiful royal palace in Spain (C)
2   Puccini opera featuring the poet Rodolfo and the seamstress Mimi (2,6) (A)
3   Describes a musical piece with little melody (C)
4   Group of musicians performing together (A)
5   Lively Spanish dance (A)
6   Electronic musical instrument resembling a piano (A)
7   Love song (A)
8   Shortened, edited (A)
9   Beethoven's *Sonata Pathétique* was used on the soundtrack of this 1940s psychological thriller (A)
10 Stringed instrument associated with Captain Corelli (A)
11 Finnish composer famed for his *Karelia Suite* and *Finlandia* (C)
12 *Die Fledermaus* features 'Adele's - - - - - - - - Song' (C)
13 Saint-Saëns wrote *The - - - - - - - - of the Animals* to amuse his friends while on holiday (A)
14 Early instrument resembling a spinet (C)

15 Nationality of the majority of the characters in *Aida* (A)
16 Contemporary of Rachmaninov whose works include *Vers la Flamme* (A)
17 Singing in a relaxed romantic manner (C)
18 Light, often humorous musical play (C)
19 Musicians such as Lang Lang and Murray Perahia (A)
20 Performer in the last round of a competition (C)
21 Instruction to play the notes sharply and detached from each other (C)
22 Ceremonial soundings of trumpets and bugles (C)
23 A tune played on bells (A)
24 Operetta containing music by Strauss about a world-famous lover (A)
25 - - - - - - - guitar, which does not have an amplifier (A)
26 Young, gifted female under the patronage or tutelage of another person (C)
27 Unaccompanied part song for several voices (C)
28 Describes a rousing, passionate piece of music (A)

QUIZ CROSSWORD

Solution on page 268.

A crossword with a twist. Work out the answer to each question in order to fill the grid.

ACROSS

7   At the 1990 World Cup, Pavarotti, Domingo and Carreras were known as the Three what? (6)

9   Which John's choral works include *Mass of the Children* and *The Gift of Life*? (6)

10   Which soprano voice is high and agile, and suited to florid delivery of Violetta at the end of Act I in *La Traviata*? (10)

11   The Last what is played on a military bugle at the end of the day? (4)

12   Which note is worth double the value of a crotchet? (5)

13   Which term describes music of the Middle Ages? (9)

15   Which Sir Michael wrote the oratorio *A Child of Our Time*? (7)

20   Which note is worth double the value of 12 Across? (9)

21   Which type of composition has a theme or themes which are developed throughout the work? (5)

23   Which notes on a brass instrument are produced without lowering a valve? (4)

24   Which 1928 opera featured music by Kurt Weill? (10)

25   Which musical term means 'quick, fast'? (6)

26   Is the first violin in the orchestra called the guider, the leader or the master? (6)

DOWN

1   Which Spanish guitarist established the instrument as one worthy of serious attention? (7)

2   Who wrote the opera *Prince Igor*? (7)

3   What was the first name of librettist Hammerstein, whose father (with the same name) was an important New York opera impresario? (5)

4   Which keyboard players are most commonly associated with church music? (9)

5   Which lyricist Sondheim collaborated with Bernstein on *West Side Story*? (7)

6   Which Handel oratorio had its premiere in Dublin in 1742? (7)

8   Whose many operas include *Don Carlos* and *Aida*? (8,5)

14   What name is given to the 'small books' which contain the words of an opera? (9)

16   Traditionally performed at twilight, which major work of this type by Monteverdi dates from 1610? (7)

17   What was the nationality of Sibelius? (7)

18   What name is given to a slow ceremonial march such as the 'Dead March' in Handel's *Saul*? (7)

19   What is a group of five musicians called? (7)

22   Which musical instrument does Julian Lloyd Webber play? (5)

WHAT CAUSED THE DEATH OF THESE CLASSICAL COMPOSERS?

Solutions on page 269.

Do you know what ended the lives of some of the classical composers? Select your guess from our multiple choice options.

1   Which composer stabbed himself in the foot with his conducting staff while beating time and died from gangrene?
2   Which composer caught a chill when he returned home late from the theatre to find his wife had locked him out of the house?
3   Which composer died from an infected pimple on his face?
4   Which composer was shot when he stepped outside one night and lit a cigar?
5   Which composer died after riding his bike into a brick wall?
6   Which composer drowned after the boat he was in was hit by a torpedo?
7   Which composer was crushed by a bookcase (or another large piece of furniture...reports vary)?
8   Which composer died at the keyboard of the organ in Notre-Dame Cathedral, Paris?
9   Which composer died from a terminal illness, on the same day that Stalin died?
10 Which composer died suddenly while dancing?
11 Which composer was injured after being struck by the carriage-pole of a horse-drawn trolley, dying several months later?
12 Which composer had a fear of the number 13 and died on Friday the 13th July?

SECTION 3: MOLTO VIVACE

(a) **César Franck**

(b) **Alexander Scriabin**

(c) **Anton Webern**

(d) **Sergei Prokofiev**

(e) **Henry Purcell**

(f) **Ernest Chausson**

(g) **Arnold Schoenberg**

(h) **Louis Vierne**

(i) **Alexander Borodin**

(j) **Jean-Baptiste Lully**

(k) **Charles-Valentin Alkan**

(l) **Enrique Granados**

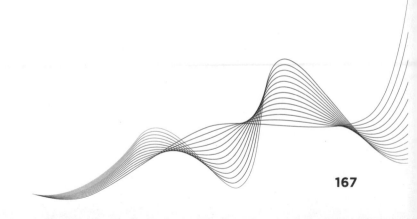

THE ULTIMATE BEETHOVEN QUIZ

Solutions on page 270.

Think you know all there is to know about Beethoven? Test your knowledge with this quiz.

1.
What year was Ludwig van Beethoven born?

a) 1780
b) 1775
c) 1770

2.
In his youth, Ludwig was taught music by his father – what was his name?

a) Christian
b) Heinrich
c) Johann

3.
How many piano concertos did Beethoven write?

a) Five
b) Six
c) Seven

4.
How did Beethoven claim to lose his hearing?

a) A recurring ear infection he'd had since childhood
b) After a fit of rage at being interrupted while working, he fell and subsequently rose to find that he was deaf
c) Continual exposure to loud orchestral noise

5.
Which piano sonata was dedicated to Count Ferdinand Ernst Gabriel von Waldstein of Vienna?

a) No. 19
b) No. 20
c) No. 21

6.
To whom was the Eroica symphony originally dedicated?

a) Louis XVIII of France
b) Archduke Rudolph of Austria
c) Napoleon Bonaparte

7.
The text Beethoven used in the finale of his Ninth Symphony was written by which poet?

a) Adelbert von Chamisso
b) Friedrich Schiller
c) Johann Wolfgang von Goethe

8.
The Royal Philharmonic Society commissioned which landmark Beethoven piece?

a) Symphony No. 9
b) *Missa Solemnis*
c) Piano Concerto No. 5

9.
In Beethoven's opera Fidelio, which character sings the aria 'Gott! Welch Dunkel hier!'?

a) Florestan
b) Pizarro
c) Leonore

10.
How many 'Late Quartets' are there?

a) Eight
b) Six
c) Four

11.
Which key is shared by the Corioian Overture, Symphony No. 5 and the Choral Fantasy?

a) D minor
b) C minor
c) E flat minor

12.
In which city was Beethoven buried after his death?

a) Vienna
b) Leipzig
c) Bonn

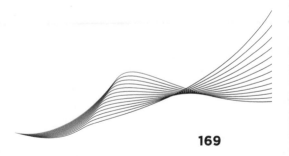

HEXACHORDS

Solution on page 270.

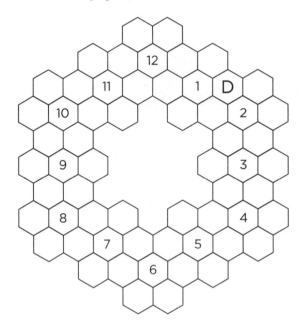

All answers have six letters and fit into the grid reading in a clockwise direction. We give you the starting point for the answer to Clue 1, but after that you have to work out in which hexagonal cell the answer begins.

CLUES

1 Composer of *On Hearing the First Cuckoo in Spring*.
2 Travelled around the country to give a series of performances.
3 Birthplace of Rachmaninov, although he spent much of his adult life abroad.
4 Nationality of composer Carl Nielsen.
5 Last part of a musical work.
6 The *1812 Overture* is about the - - - - - - of Napoleon.
7 Repeated the actual words spoken.
8 Not softly. Fortissimo!
9 If the instruction says Allegro, you play in a - - - - - - manner.
10 Written comment by a critic after a performance.
11 Leopold was the - - - - - - of Wolfgang in a famous family.
12 Which musical instrument is Joaquín Rodrigo most associated with, although he never learned to play it?

SESTET

Solution on page 271.

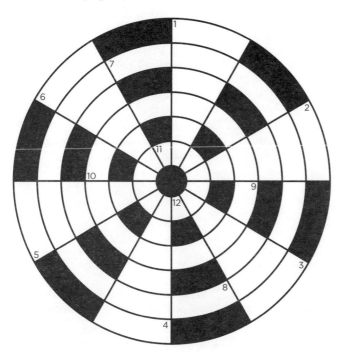

All answers have six letters. 1 to 6 start in the outer circle
and are written toward the centre. 7 to 12 go around the rings
in a clockwise direction.

CLUES

1   Who wrote the *Water Music*?
2   In which country was Delibes born?
3   Cry from an audience when they want more!
4   English composer and pacifist with the first name of Frank, who died in 1941.
5   Lauren Zhang was the ------ of Young Musician of the Year 2018.
6   Strauss opera first performed in Dresden in 1905.
7   One who gives financial support to an artist or organization.
8   Name by which Beethoven's 3rd Symphony is better known.
9   Puccini's *La Fanciulla del West*, is also sometimes known as *The Girl of the*
    ------ *West*.
10 These 12 symphonies by Haydn bear the name of a capital city.
11 The cover of a long-playing vinyl record.
12 First name of Beatles producer Martin, who composed the score for the
    Bond movie *Live and Let Die*.

THE ULTIMATE CLASSICAL MUSIC QUIZ

Solutions on page 271.

Fancy yourself a bit of a classical music expert? You're going to love this quiz.

1.
Which of these is not the subtitle of a Haydn symphony?

a) Hornsignal
b) Lamentatione
c) Tragic
d) Mercury

2.
Which of Elgar's Enigma Variations was partially inspired by a bulldog?

a) Variation XI (G.R.S.)
b) Variation I (C.A.E.)
c) Variation XII (B.G.N.)
d) Variation IX (Nimrod)

3.
Where was cellist Jaqueline du Pré born?

a) Cheltenham
b) Oxford
c) Cambridge
d) Cirencester

4.
Which conductor always appeared on the podium wearing a white carnation?

a) Sir Thomas Beecham
b) Sir Malcolm Sargent
c) Sir Charles Mackerras
d) Sir John Barbirolli

5.
How old was Giuseppe Verdi when he wrote his Requiem?

a) 50
b) 60
c) 70
d) 80

6.
What is the name given to the lower register of the clarinet's playing range?

a) Chalumeau
b) Thalumeau
c) Shalumeau
d) Shalamar

7.
What did Benjamin Britten use to simulate raindrops in his opera for amateur musicians, Noye's Fludde?

a) Pipettes and buckets
b) Empty baked beans tins
c) Teacups on a string
d) A typewriter

8.
Who wrote a piece called the 'Skittle Alley Trio'?

a) Wolfgang Amadeus Mozart
b) George Gershwin
c) Leonard Bernstein
d) Antonin Dvořák

9.
In French opera houses, what job does the Souffler have?

a) To encourage applause
b) Prompter
c) First-aider
d) Dessert chef

10.
What is Simon Rattle's middle name?

a) Denis
b) David
c) Derek
d) Daniel

11.
What subtitle goes with Gilbert & Sullivan's operetta The Pirates of Penzance?

a) *The Witch's Curse*
b) *The Lass That Loved a Sailor*
c) *The Slave of Duty*
d) *The Peer and the Peri*

12.
Which composer wrote two piano concertos, one violin concerto and one double concerto for violin and cello?

a) Beethoven
b) Brahms
c) Bach
d) Bruch

13.
In which country was Delibes's opera Lakmé set?

a) Ceylon
b) Burma
c) India
d) Vietnam

14.
Which of these vehicles did Herbert von Karajan not appear with on the cover of one of his recordings?

a) Airplane
b) Boat
c) Racing car
d) Hovercraft

15.
How many Ballades did Chopin write?

a) 4
b) 12
c) 24
d) 48

16.
Which of these actors has not played Beethoven on screen?

a) John Belushi
b) Gary Oldman
c) Ed Harris
d) Simon Callow

17.

In Purcell's Dido and Aeneas, Dido is Queen of where?

a) Carthage
b) Egypt
c) Troy
d) Rome

18.

In which year did the Sydney Opera House open?

a) 1971
b) 1972
c) 1973
d) 1974

19.

Which of these composers was given the title of Master of the Queen's Music?

a) W S Gilbert
b) Sir Walter Parratt
c) Frank Bridge
d) Harold Darke

20.

Which of these artists did not perform with Luciano Pavarotti during his lifetime?

a) Sheryl Crow
b) Celine Dion
c) The Spice Girls
d) Madonna

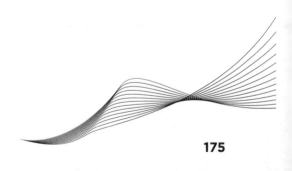

METRONOME

Solution on page 272.

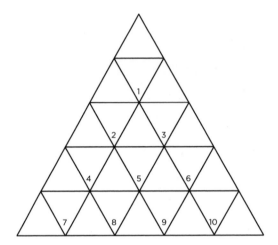

Each answer contains four letters. The first letter goes in a numbered triangle, the second letter directly above it, the third letter to the right and the fourth to the left.

CLUES

1   Source of inspiration for creative artists.
2   Main performer in a musical.
3   Borodin's musical journey, *In the Steppes of Central* - - - -.
4   Original thought.
5   Title awarded to Kiri Te Kanawa.
6   Movie.
7   In short, *Fantasia*'s creator, Mr Disney.
8   Sound made by ringing bells.
9   Soprano noted for early music, - - - - Kirkby.
10   Dance of the Sugar - - - - Fairy.

HEXACHORDS

Solution on page 272.

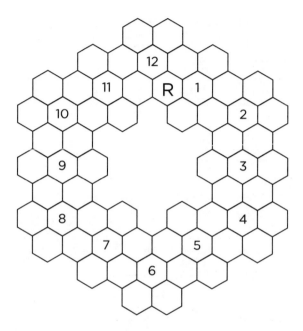

All answers have six letters and fit into the grid reading in a clockwise direction. We give you the starting point for the answer to Clue 1, but after that you have to work out in which hexagonal cell the answer begins.

CLUES

1 First name of composer Schumann.
2 Continue playing where you left off.
3 Film theatre where an organ provided the music in its early days.
4 Receipt to give you entry to a concert.
5 Conductor Sir Simon.
6 Verdi's 'Chorus of the - - - - - - Slaves' is from his opera *Nabucco*.
7 Classical ballet - - - - - - *and the Beast*.
8 First name of Welsh tenor Burrows.
9 Recurring notes or melodies in a composition.
10 Fairy tale by the Brothers Grimm commemorated in a statue in the town of the title, 'The Town Musicians of - - - - - -'.
11 Émile Waldteufel composed a waltz for this winter sportsperson.
12 Czech composer Antonin - - - - - -.

QUIZ CROSSWORD

Solution on page 273.

A crossword with a twist. Work out the answer to each question in order to fill the grid.

ACROSS

7 What precedes 'in excelsis Deo' in the hymn of praise? (6)

9 What is the first name of English pianist Miss Cooper? (6)

10 With what might a percussionist strike the timpani? (10)

11 If you see an 'f' on a music score will the music be loud or soft? (4)

12 Which name goes with *Grimes* in the title of an opera about a fisherman in Aldeburgh, Suffolk, England? (5)

13 What name is given to the simultaneous combinations of notes which produce a pleasing effect? (9)

15 What is another name for violins? (7)

20 Which oratorio by J S Bach relates to the nativity? (9)

21 Which fishers are the subject of a work by Bizet? (5)

23 Which Latin word for work is used with a number to identify a piece? (4)

24 Who wrote the music for the movie *633 Squadron*? (3,7)

25 In which city was Johann Strauss born? (6)

26 Which John gave his name to a theme in the film *Dances with Wolves*? (6)

DOWN

1 A curved line over a group of notes shows that the notes are what? (7)

2 Which name of a musical instrument precedes '*Voluntary*' in the piece by Jeremiah Clarke also known as the *Prince of Denmark's March*? (7)

3 Which dance is in triple time? (5)

4 Which word completes the name of an opera by Benjamin Britten, *A - - - - - - - - - Night's Dream*? (9)

5 Which French composer wrote the ballet *Les Biches*? (7)

6 Which funeral piece was unfinished by Mozart and was a work of note by Fauré? (7)

8 Who wrote *The Mastersingers of Nuremberg*? (7,6)

14 Parry, Delius and Elgar were all born during which royal period? (9)

16 Which famous comedy actor shared the Oscar for the music for the film *Limelight*? (7)

17 Which 1982 film starring Jack Lemmon and Sissy Spacek had a music score by Vangelis? (7)

18 Which special day at Troldhaugen is the subject of a song by Grieg? (7)

19 What completes the title of the Handel piece 'The - - - - - - - of the Queen of Sheba'? (7)

22 Is the last movement of Mozart's Sonata No. 11 in A major called the Turkish Fugue, Rondo or Tempo? (5)

THE CLASSICAL MUSIC GENERAL KNOWLEDGE QUIZ

Solutions on page 273.

How niche is your knowledge of classical music and composers? This quiz will give you some food for thought...

1.
As a young man, Johann Sebastian Bach walked more than 400km (250 miles) from Arnstadt to Lübeck to hear which musical idol?

a)   Buxtehude
b)   Corelli
c)   Schütz
d)   Vivaldi

2.
Danish composer Carl Nielsen took up which hobby to lower his heart rate?

a)   Chess
b)   Knitting
c)   Yoga
d)   Dancing

3.
According to caloriecount.com, how many calories do you burn by playing the violin for an hour?

a)   1,250
b)   325
c)   52
d)   175

4.
And how many calories do you think you burn playing a bigger instrument, the cello?

a)   440
b)   140
c)   340
d)   240

5.
Eccentric French composer Erik Satie had an unusual diet for good health – what was it?

a)   He was on the Paleo diet
b)   He only ate white food
c)   He only drank soup
d)   He only ate meat

6.
After lunch each day, Beethoven would enjoy a long, vigorous walk in the countryside. What is he said to have always brought with him?

a)   A pencil and manuscript
b)   A pocket score of Bach's *Well-Tempered Clavier*
c)   An ear-trumpet
d)   A flask of coffee

7.

They say early mornings are the key to success – which composer would start work at 6am having gone to bed only five hours earlier?

a) Wagner
b) Mozart
c) Fanny Mendelssohn
d) Scriabin

8.

Which composer rose at dawn and broke his fast with a cup of coffee – using exactly 60 beans, it is reported, which he prepared himself?

a) Tchaikovsky
b) Philip Glass
c) Schubert
d) Beethoven

9.

How did Wagner choose to greet his wife Cosima on the morning of one of her birthdays?

a) He filled her room with sweet-smelling flowers
b) He commissioned the Tonhalle Orchester Zürich to perform one of his compositions for her on their staircase
c) He recited the great Germanic Nordic sagas
d) He brought her breakfast in bed

10.

At the beginning of Act III of Puccini's La Bohème, it's the dawn of a snowy morning just outside Paris. Mimi is meeting her lover. What's the name of her lover?

a) Alfredo
b) Rodolfo
c) Roberto
d) Marcello

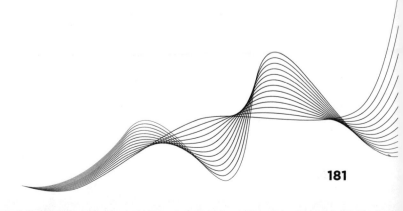

OCTET

Solution on page 274.

SECTION 3: MOLTO VIVACE

Solve the clues below to find the eight-letter answers. The first letter of the answer goes in the numbered square, and the answer can go clockwise or anticlockwise. We tell you if it is (C) clockwise or (A) anticlockwise.

CLUES

1 Opening piece of music (C)
2 Return to the spotlight by a performer who has been absent (C)
3 1978 film with Christopher Reeve and a John Williams soundtrack (C)
4 One who sings in the Swiss mountains (C)
5 *A Garland for Joey* is the songbook for which show? (3,5) (C)
6 Short romantic composition usually for piano (C)
7 It is used to pluck the strings of a guitar (A)
8 Brass instrument with a slide (C)
9 Singer (C)
10 Verdi's *La* - - - - - - - - is based on the play *La Dame aux Camelias* (A)
11 Male voice higher than the normal range (A)
12 Stage, podium (C)
13 Small double-headed instrument, which is beaten (4,4) (C)
14 Sections within a piece of music (A)
15 Note played for half as long as a minim (C)

16 Australian-born classical guitarist John, who recorded with Julian Bream (A)
17 Traditional ballad (4,4) (C)
18 Nationality of percussionist Dame Evelyn Glennie (A)
19 Played a guitar or similar instrument (A)
20 Jay Ungar's 'Ashokan - - - - - - - -' provided the soundtrack for the 1990 PBS mini-series *The Civil War* (A)
21 James Horner and Jerry Goldsmith wrote music for this movie franchise (4,4) (C)
22 The coronation march *Crown - - - - - - - - -* was composed by William Walton (A)
23 Repetition of a phrase or melody at a lower or higher pitch (A)
24 Famous song from Bizet's *Carmen* (A)
25 Person who publicizes a concert or tour (A)
26 A lullaby or cradle song (C)
27 First name of classical pianist Grosvenor (C)
28 Individual who is one half of a performance by two (C)

ENIGMA VARIATIONS

Solution on page 274.

A cryptic crossword.

ACROSS

7 Marriage reported in French newspaper (6)
9 Loan at risk with no key at all (6)
10 Stormy Beethoven sonata (3,7)
11 Flowing cape keeps momentum (4)
12 English interpretation of Verdi (5)
13 Unfussy vocal piece in church (9)
16 See Gill twirling around in the ballet (7)
21 I own range which comes from Scandinavia like Peer Gynt (9)
22 Carol's midwinter at Charles Dickens's house? (5)
24 Got to their feet, we hear, in lines (4)
25 Compress carton to play it (7,3)
26 Listen carefully to this Christmas night (6)
27 Caribbean buccaneer or an illegal radio station (6)

DOWN

1 Lyric hardly revealed by this member of the Strauss family (7)
2 Business associate on the dance floor? (7)
3 1066 invader loses a point in Bellini's opera (5)
4 Role for Estonian composer (4)
5 Calm yourself and write music (7)
6 *Romeo and Juliet* scene played in the dress circle (7)
8 Unhappy Viennese river? (3,4,6)
14 Lies around Rachmaninov's symphonic poem of the dead (4)
15 Burst into song after cocktail gins (4)
17 Brood in appraisal of Russian genius (7)
18 Dance on a tiny staircase (3,4)
19 Quick, real log is broken up (7)
20 Gave tot to produce a dance (7)
23 Item possibly appears with rhythm (5)
25 Hardens scenes on stage (4)

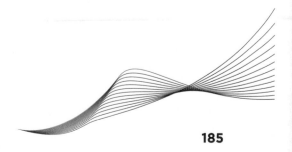

QUIZ CROSSWORD

Solution on page 275.

A crossword with a twist. Work out the answer to each question in order to fill the grid.

ACROSS

7   What music term means 'connected smoothly with neither a break nor a stress'? (6)

9   Which knighted conductor - - - - - - Boult features in the film *The Point of the Stick*? (6)

10   Which two-word expression means a serious all-sung epic work? (5,5)

11   What is the lowest male voice? (4)

12   Steinway and Bechstein are famous makers of which musical instrument? (5)

13   Which legendary villain, who killed six of his brides, is the subject of a one-act opera by Bartók? (9)

15   What boat is manned by a serenading singer on the canals of Venice? (7)

20   Which woodwind instruments have also been called fipple flutes? (9)

21   An operetta is also referred to as what kind of opera, light or clear? (5)

23   Which word completes the name of Hubert Parry's anthem from 1902, 'I Was - - - -'? (4)

24   What keyboard stringed instrument was widely used from the 15th to the 18th centuries? (10)

25   Which Ravel masterpiece produced a perfect score for ice dancers Torvill and Dean at the 1984 Winter Olympics? (6)

26   Who shared the title of the Humperdinck opera with Hansel? (6)

DOWN

1   What is another name for a chorus? (7)

2   The sound of which weapons makes a loud contribution to the *1812 Overture*? (7)

3   What are performances by individuals called? (5)

4   Which name for a short, light piece of music shares its name with a table-top game? (9)

5   What are the highest voices, especially of boys and girls, called? (7)

6   Which Italian word for master is used to describe a distinguished musician? (7)

8   In English, the title of which work by Johann Strauss means 'The Bat'? (3,10)

14   In the 20th century, Bernstein and Stokowski were famously flamboyant when they took on which directorial role? (9)

16   Who abandoned medical studies for music, and whose works include *Symphonie Fantastique*? (7)

17   Which military man completes the title of the theatre piece by Stravinsky titled *The - - - - - - -'s Tale*? (7)

18   Which composer - - - - - - - Nyman wrote the opera *The Man Who Mistook His Wife for a Hat*? (7)

19   What was the first name of French composer Gounod? (7)

22   Who wrote *The Watermill*, and also the theme 'Sailing By' for the BBC Radio 4 Shipping Forecast? (5)

A QUIZ FOR CLASSICAL MUSIC EXPERTS

Solutions on page 276.

A gruelling musical theory quiz. If you get full marks in this quiz, you should seriously consider becoming a musician.

1.
This key signature is the enharmonic equivalent of which other key signature?

a)   F sharp major
b)   D flat major
c)   B flat major
d)   B major

2.
If you play something 'col legno', what are you doing?

a)   Playing with a mute
b)   Playing the bow on the string
c)   Playing with force
d)   Hitting the strings with the wooden side of your violin bow

3.
A wind quintet is typically made up of which five instruments?

a)   Flute, oboe, two clarinets and bassoon
b)   Flute, two oboes, clarinet and bassoon
c)   Flute, oboe, clarinet, horn and bassoon
d)   Two flutes, oboe, clarinet and horn

4.
If a piece of music is marked *mancando*, what should you do?

a)   Fade away
b)   Emphasize the note
c)   Play gradually more slowly
d)   Play solemnly

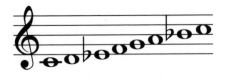

5.
What mode is this?
a)   Lydian
b)   Mixolydian
c)   Dorian
d)   Phrygian

6.
How many symphonies did Beethoven write?

a) 9
b) 10
c) 11
d) 12

7.
What is the relative minor of this key?

a) A sharp minor
b) D sharp minor
c) G sharp minor
d) E sharp minor

8.
Which of the following composers did not write a Ninth Symphony?

a) Bruckner
b) Vaughan Williams
c) Mozart
d) Sibelius

9.
What chord is this?

a) A minor
b) E minor
c) C major
d) F major

10.
What kind of chord is this?

a) Tristan chord
b) Elektra chord
c) Petrushka chord
d) Augmented chord

SESTET

Solution on page 276.

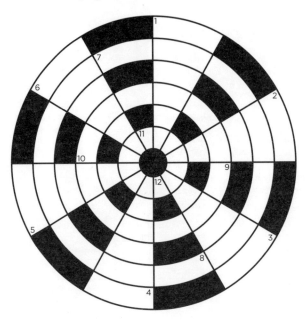

All answers have six letters. 1 to 6 start in the outer circle and are written toward the centre. 7 to 12 go around the rings in a clockwise direction.

CLUES

1 Which composer had the names Wolfgang and Amadeus?

2 Handel wrote *Julius - - - - - - in Egypt*.

3 Which Italian, born in 1873, became the first operatic tenor to be recorded on gramophone records?

4 The musical *Cabaret* was based on the play *I Am a - - - - - -*.

5 What name is given to an emphasis on a musical note, also called an accent?

6 The pianist and composer Paderewski became Prime Minister of where in 1919?

7 Which musical composition is usually in four parts and incorporates a keyboard?

8 Which form of entertainment includes military music and marching?

9 Which first name completes the title of the Tchaikovsky opera *- - - - - - Onegin*?

10 Which Spanish cellist with the first name of Pablo wrote the oratorio *The Manger*?

11 Which sound system has more than one speaker?

12 Singers in good voice might be said to have - - - - - - the roof!

SECTION 3: MOLTO VIVACE

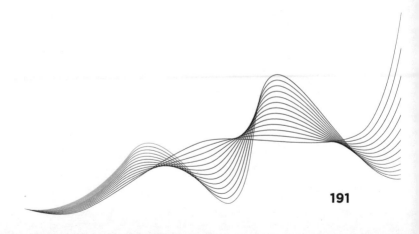

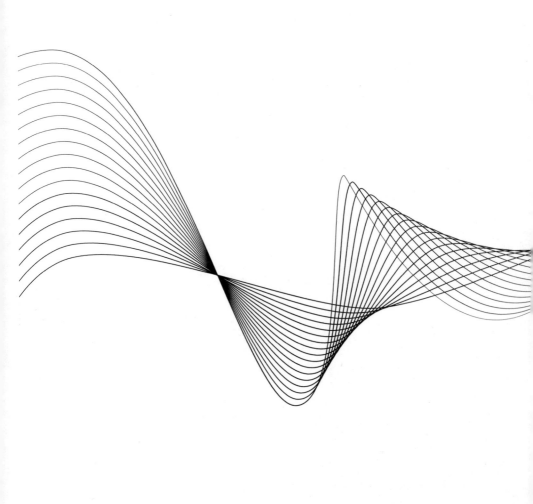

SOLUTIONS

SECTION ONE

ADAGIO

PRESTO

ACROSS

6   Season
7   Hear
9   Busker
10 Rocks
12 Read
13 Choir
17 Pause
18 Solo
21 Opera
22 Record
24 Lake
25 Penned

DOWN

1   Natural
2   Book
3   Refrain
4   Track
5   Glass
8   Orchestra
11 Art
14 Karaoke
15 Soprano
16 Bow
19 Sound
20 Bells
23 Crew

SUDO-KEY

mn	C	D	E	A	G	B	mj	F
B	A	mj	mn	C	F	D	G	E
E	G	F	mj	D	B	A	mn	C
mj	D	mn	G	F	C	E	A	B
A	E	G	D	B	mn	F	C	mj
C	F	B	A	mj	E	mn	D	G
D	mn	C	B	E	mj	G	F	A
G	mj	E	F	mn	A	C	B	D
F	B	A	C	G	D	mj	E	mn

NOTATION

BEETHOVEN. BAGATELLE

A CLASS ACT

FRANCESCA / FRIDAY / 7.00PM / VIOLIN

CLARA / TUESDAY / 11.00AM / DRUMS

FRANZ / THURSDAY / 4.00PM / CELLO

LOUISE / MONDAY / 8.30PM / TROMBONE

CARL / WEDNESDAY / 7.30PM / SAXOPHONE

CYMBALISM

LUTE, FLUTE, TRIANGLE, GUITAR.

MISSING VOICES

FALSTAFF (VERDI)

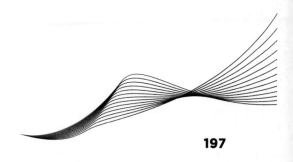

NUMBER NAMES

ALLEGRI = 24.

E = 1, G = 2, L = 3, A = 4, R = 5, I = 6.

BACH

1	BACH	15	STOP
2	AREA	16	HOPE
3	CELL	17	ABET
4	HALF	18	BACH
5	MOTH	19	ECHO
6	OBOE	20	THOR
7	TOUR	21	BACH
8	HERA	22	AIRY
9	BACH	23	CRAM
10	ADZE	24	HYMN
11	CZAR	25	EDIT
12	HERB	26	DARE
13	FISH	27	IRIS
14	INTO	28	TEST

THE CLASSIC FM HALL OF FAME

```
V A U G H A N W I L L I A M S        W
  N   O       I           U      B A C H
E L G A R     L A U R I D S E N  L   A
  A   N       L           S      T   N
B A R B E R   I           K O R N G O L D
U     R   H A R V E Y     R      N     E
T   G     M             G   P          L
T A L L I S   S T R A U S S   A   C
E   A     T       O       K   C O H E N
R   S     R   H E S S     Y   H   O
W I S E M A N     S           E   P
O       V     M I T C H E L L L   I
R   D E L I U S   N   O       B I N G E
T       N     I   P           E     R
H   Z   S     G   L           L     S
  R I M S K Y K O R S A K O V     W   S
    M     Y       U   N         I   H
    M       E I N A U D I       D   W
    E             O       B O R O D I N
P A R T     R O D R I G O       R   N
```

SCREEN TEST

CYMBALISM

NOTE, TENOR, SERENADE, SOPRANO.

MISSING VOICES

TOSCA (PUCCINI)

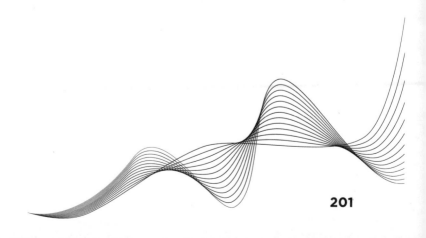

RAFFLE PRIZES

048 / WHITE / CHORAL MUSIC CONCERT.

085 / GREEN / PIANO RECITAL.

126 / BLUE / GUITAR RECITAL.

197 / PINK / VIOLIN CONCERT.

ADDERS

ANTHEM

MAJOR SEVENTH

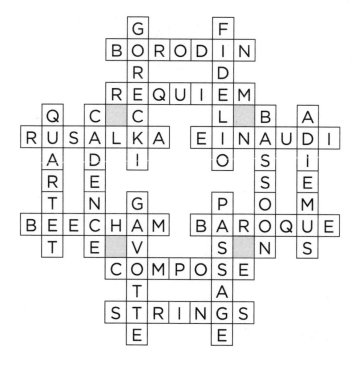

NOTATION

OFFENBACH. LA BELLE HELENE

MUSIC MAKERS

1 / CÉCILE / PIANO / FOUR YEARS.

2 / ALEXANDER / GUITAR / TWO YEARS.

3 / GEORGE / FLUTE / TEN YEARS.

4 / ALMA / VIOLIN / EIGHT YEARS.

MISSING VOICES

BLUEBEARD'S CASTLE (BARTÓK)

NOTATION

BARBER. DOVER BEACH

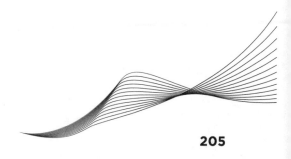

RING CYCLE

1   Organ
2   Angel
3   Elope
4   Peach
5   Choir
6   Irate
7   Tepid
8   Ideas
9   Aside
10   Decor

M FOR MUSIC

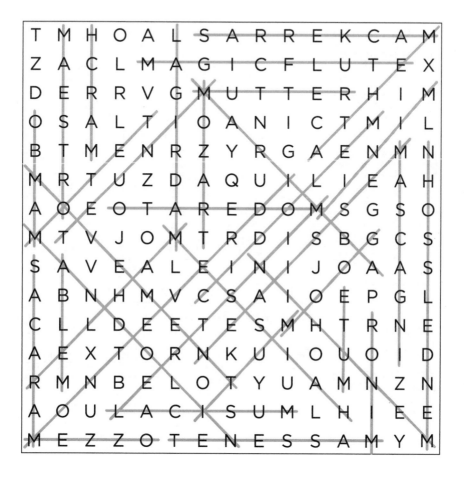

INSTRUMENTAL

```
        B       B U G L E     O C A R I N A
C Y M B A L S       L           H
    A     S     V I O L I N     I     H O R N
L Y R E S       C               M     A
U     I     O   V   K E T T L E D R U M S
T A M B O U R I N E       H     S     M     P
E     B     N       N     E           O     I
      A             L   S A X O P H O N E   N
        C       H A R P     R   A   I       E
        I       U       I   B   R   C       T
Z I T H E R     C E L L O   P I A N O
        T       D       L       S           C
O B O E         V   B   P I C C O L O       O
    A   R       G U I T A R     C           R
    G   N       U   R   N       H   K       N
    P   R       R   G   J   T R O M B O N E
S I T A R       D   I   O   A       R   T   T
    P   Y       N   B   D   O
    E           A   O
    S H A W M   L   C O R A N G L A I S
```

CYMBALISM

HARP, SHARP, PHRASE, RHAPSODY.

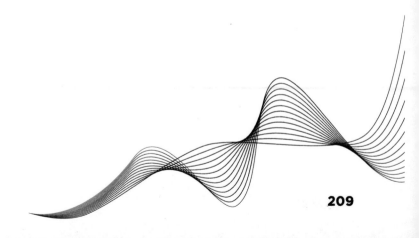

SUDO-KEY

F	B	E	C	mj	mn	A	G	D
mj	G	A	D	B	F	mn	C	E
mn	C	D	E	A	G	F	mj	B
E	F	B	A	D	mj	G	mn	C
G	D	mj	F	mn	C	E	B	A
A	mn	C	G	E	B	mj	D	F
D	mj	F	B	G	E	C	A	mn
B	E	G	mn	C	A	D	F	mj
C	A	mn	mj	F	D	B	E	G

OPERA IN THE PARK

1 / ELENA / UMBRELLA A.

2 / ANTONIO / UMBRELLA B.

3 / GUSTAV / UMBRELLA C.

4 / ROSE / UMBRELLA D.

ADDERS

BUGLES

MAJOR SEVENTH

KARAJAN
PIE JESU
LULLABY
ROMANCE
DELIBES
FIDDLER
RODRIGO
LISTENS
MARIMBA
PASSION
JUPITER
CLASSIC
BALLADE
OCTAVES
SEGOVIA
SINGING

NUMBER NAMES

SONATA = 22.
N = 1, O = 2, T = 3, E = 4, A = 5, S = 6

STUDENT SHARE

Rooms in order when moving left to right along the floor.
Third floor: Sofia, Mikhail, Nikolai.
Second floor: Diana, Peter, Sergei.
First floor: Maurice, Elizabeth, Julia.

NOTATION

CAGE. BACCHANALE

ADDERS

PASTORAL

CONDUCTORS

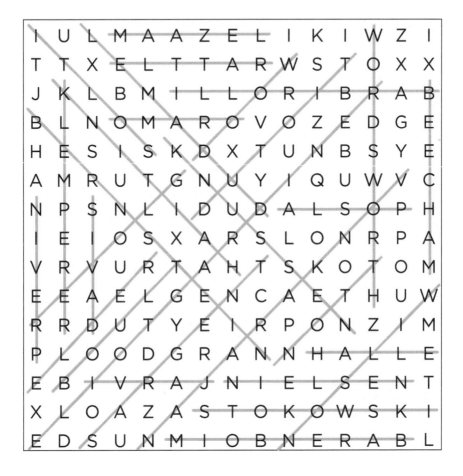

CHOIR PRACTICE

1	Bass		15	Polo
2	Area		16	Snow
3	Sell		17	Trap
4	Salt		18	Rill
5	Mass		19	Alto
6	Alto		20	Plod
7	Star		21	Bass
8	Sort		22	Alto
9	Alas		23	Stew
10	Lull		24	Sown
11	Alto		25	Wasp
12	Slob		26	Alto
13	Tips		27	Stop
14	Iron		28	Pope

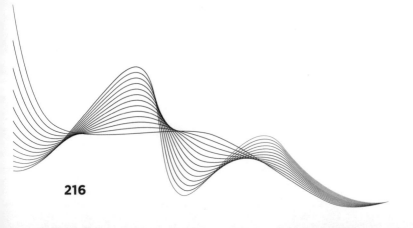

SUDO-KEY

mj	mn	E	D	C	B	G	A	F
A	B	G	mn	E	F	C	D	mj
D	C	F	G	mj	A	mn	B	E
mn	A	C	E	G	mj	B	F	D
G	F	B	C	A	D	E	mj	mn
E	mj	D	F	B	mn	A	C	G
F	G	A	mj	mn	C	D	E	B
C	E	mj	B	D	G	F	mn	A
B	D	mn	A	F	E	mj	G	C

ON TOUR

1 / HENRY / PLANE D / NORWAY.

2 / MARIANA / PLANE B / ITALY.

3 / LAURA / PLANE C / AUSTRIA.

4 / DAVID / PLANE A / FRANCE.

NUMBER NAMES

ALLEGRETTO = 42.

A = 3, L = 1, G = 4, R = 2, E = 6, T = 7, O = 5.

NOTATION

WEBER. OBERON

ADDERS

FINALE

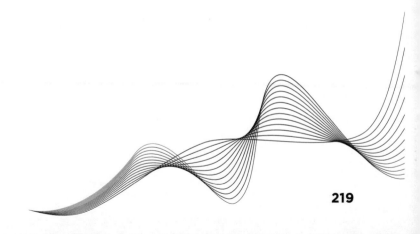

MAJOR SEVENTH

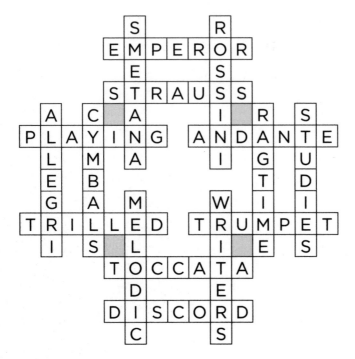

QUIZ NIGHT

FIRST / BAROQUE CHICKS / RUSSIAN MUSIC.

SECOND / NO STRINGS / ELGAR.

THIRD / THE FIDDLERS / MOZART.

FOURTH / BEST BATONS / PURCELL.

FIFTH / THE TIMPS / FILM MUSIC.

MUSIC BOXES

1	Item	15	Riot
2	Tuba	16	Pats
3	Ebbs	17	Lute
4	Mash	18	Upon
5	Crop	19	Told
6	Robe	20	Ends
7	Oboe	21	Slip
8	Peel	22	Lyre
9	Drum	23	Iris
10	Rise	24	Pest
11	Uses	25	Sage
12	Mess	26	Agog
13	Harp	27	Gong
14	Asia	28	Eggs

MISSING VOICES

LA TRAVIATA (VERDI)

ADDERS

TRIPLETS

UNFINISHED SYMPHONY

The missing word is SURPRISE.

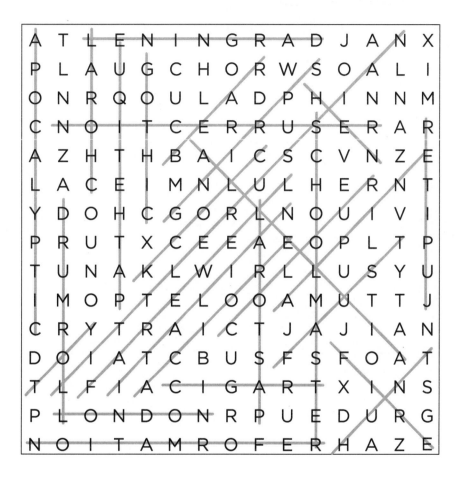

NUMBER NAMES

SAINT-SAENS = 46.

I = 1, E = 2, N = 3, T = 4, M = 5, A = 6, S = 7.

SUDO-KEY

C	F	A	mj	D	E	G	mn	B
D	G	mj	mn	A	B	E	F	C
mn	B	E	G	F	C	A	D	mj
A	mn	D	B	G	F	mj	C	E
G	mj	F	E	C	A	D	B	mn
B	E	C	D	mj	mn	F	G	A
mj	C	G	A	B	D	mn	E	F
E	D	B	F	mn	mj	C	A	G
F	A	mn	C	E	G	B	mj	D

MUSICAL MEMORABILIA

FLORENCE / 17 / SHEET MUSIC / £30
CLAUDE / 12 / POSTER / £10
HEATHER / 59 / T-SHIRTS / £60
JOHANN / 42 / BOOKS / £100
LILI / 21 / VINYL RECORDS / £20

ADDERS

CARMEN

JUST THE TICKET

1 / LEONARD / £16 TICKET / SATURDAY / B8.

2 / SUZANNA / £20 TICKET / WEDNESDAY / C2.

3 / RACHEL / £6 TICKET / THURSDAY / C3.

4 / FREDERIK / £10 TICKET / FRIDAY / B7.

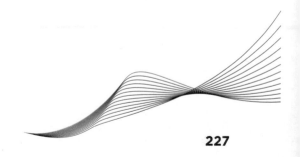

THE SHOW MUST GO ON

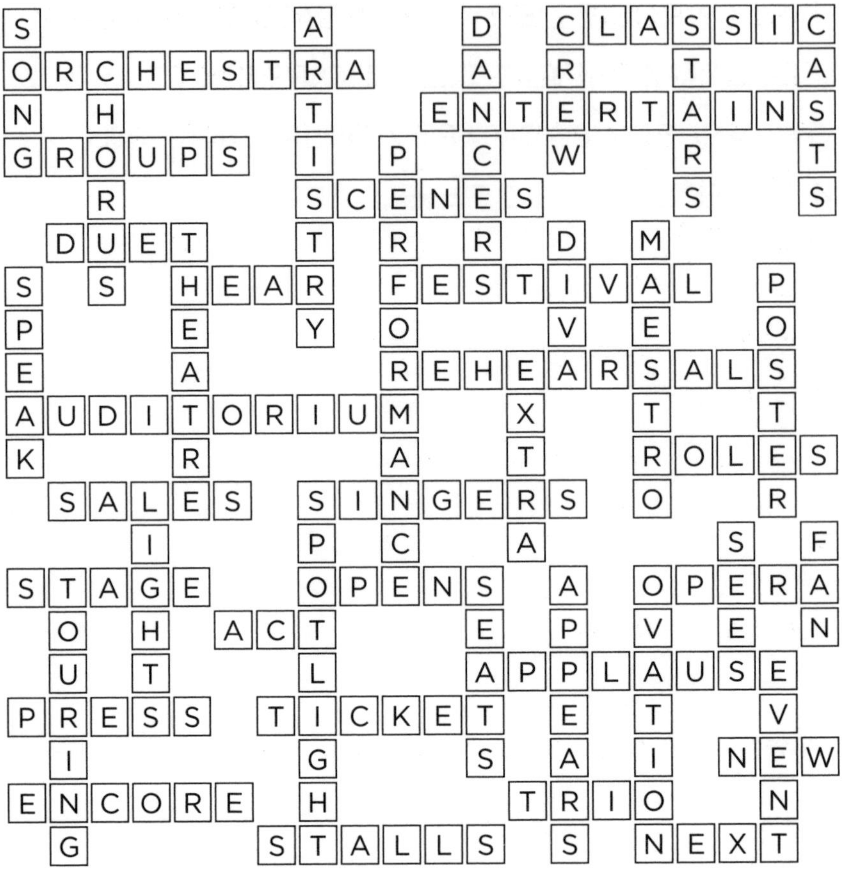

ON CUE

FIRST / ROSIE / £12 / THE FILM SOUNDTRACK.

SECOND / THEA / £32 / CHOIR MUSIC.

THIRD / EDWARD / £20 / OPERA ARIAS AND DUETS.

FOURTH / JOHANNES / £16 / VIVALDI'S *FOUR SEASONS*.

LAST / ISABELLA / £40 / PUCCINI'S *LA BOHÈME*.

NOTATION

BAX. THE GARDEN OF FAND

SPOT THE DIFFERENCE

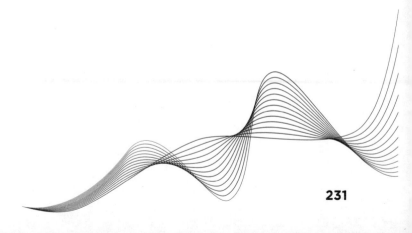

SOLUTIONS

SECTION TWO

ACCELERANDO

CODA

Donizetti is the coded composer.

CODE: 1/H, 2/A, 3/R, 4/P, 5/S, 6/Y, 7/I, 8/C, 9/N, 10/G, 11/U, 12/L, 13/O, 14/E, 15/X, 16/T, 17/J, 18/D, 19/F, 20/K, 21/Q, 22/Z, 23/M, 24/V, 25/B, 26/W.

Words formed, reading from left to right and from top to bottom of the grid:

ACROSS
Asparagus
Harp
Exterior
Sphere
Candy
Purpose
Fee
Algebra
Share
Weasel
Embezzle
Purr
Itinerary

DOWN
Physician
Orphanage
Sleek
Antique
Acre
Upon
Potassium
Jewellery
Pea
Freezer
Swear
Omit
Vein

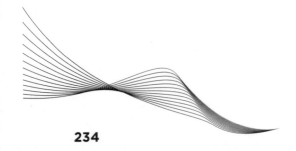

RING CYCLE

1   Verdi
2   Ditch
3   Chest
4   Stoop
5   Opera
6   Radar
7   Aroma
8   Mauve
9   Verse
10   Serve

COMPOSER OR PASTA?

1   Tuffoli: **Pasta**
2   Bertoncini: **Composer**
3   Bucatini: **Pasta**
4   Sorprese: **Pasta**
5   Capellini: **Pasta**
6   Testaroli: **Pasta**
7   Piccinni: **Composer**
8   Zitoni: **Pasta**
9   Filini: **Pasta**
10   Mercadante: **Composer**
11   Pizzetti: **Composer**
12   Pinottini: **Composer**
13   Dragonetti: **Composer**
14   Campagnoli: **Composer**
15   Bazzini: **Composer**

HIDDEN INSTRUMENT

ZITHER

PRESTO

ACROSS:

6	London
7	Diva
9	Wagner
10	Elgar
12	Alto
13	Oscar
17	Grieg
18	Lyre
21	Bream
22	Danube
24	Owen
25	Stylus

DOWN:

1	Andante
2	Horn
3	Wiseman
4	Largo
5	Score
8	Crescendo
11	Bax
14	Trumpet
15	Cymbals
16	Bee
19	Oboes
20	Tenor
23	Note

COMPOSITION

The composer is MOZART.

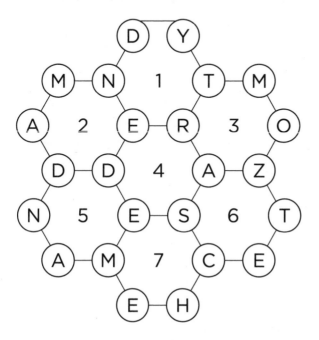

1 Trendy
2 Damned
3 Mozart
4 Erased
5 Demand
6 Aztecs
7 Scheme

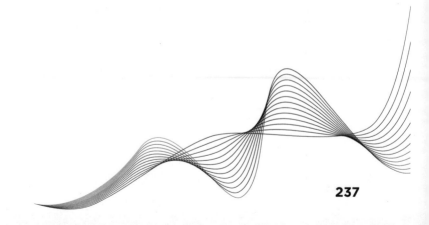

CYMBALISM

TRIO, ORATORIO, CONTRALTO, CONCERTO.

CAN YOU GUESS THE OPERA FROM THE EMOJIS?

1   *The Marriage of Figaro*
2   *Eugene Onegin*
3   *The Barber of Seville*
4   *Madam Butterfly*
5   *The Cunning Little Vixen*
6   *Tristan and Isolde*
7   *Hansel and Gretel*
8   *The Magic Flute*
9   *Carmen*
10 *La Traviata*
11 *Orphée et Eurydice*

RING CYCLE

1 *Tosca*
2 Canal
3 Alpha
4 Haifa
5 Faust
6 Stale
7 Leash
8 Shiny
9 Nymph
10 Photo

CAN YOU PUT THE INSTRUMENT IN ITS RIGHT PLACE IN THE ORCHESTRA?

a) First violin: 1
b) Flute: 4
c) Oboe: 15
d) Tuba: 12
e) Harp: 2
f) Piano: 6
g) Viola: 16
h) Double bass: 13

i) Cello: 17
j) Trumpet: 9
k) Trombone: 11
l) Horn: 8
m) Percussion: 7
n) Bassoon: 14
o) Clarinet: 5
p) Second violin: 3

HIDDEN COMPOSER

SMETANA

CODA

The Magic Flute is the coded opera.

CODE: 1/S, 2/I, 3/N, 4/G, 5/O, 6/T, 7/C, 8/H, 9/D, 10/V, 11/R, 12/J, 13/K, 14/X, 15/W, 16/P, 17/Y, 18/Q, 19/Z, 20/U, 21/M, 22/A, 23/F, 24/L, 25/B, 26/E.

Words formed, reading from left to right and from top to bottom of the grid:

ACROSS	DOWN
Discovery	Espionage
Sing	Incognito
Objector	Ivory
Isobar	Cajoled
Ninth	Vice
Mexican	Rook
Fad	Acquitted
Gateway	Anonymous
Spurn	May
Custom	Farming
Interior	Acres
Menu	Undo
Zoologist	Zeal

COMPOSITION

The composer is MAHLER.

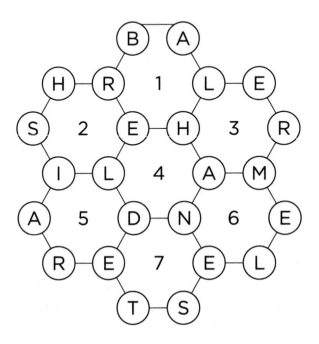

1   Herbal
2   Relish
3   Mahler
4   Handle
5   Derail
6   Enamel
7   Nested

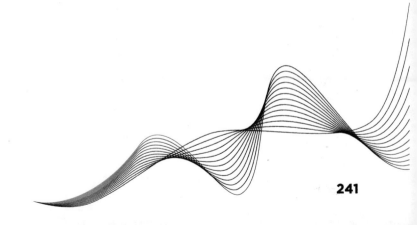

HIDDEN OPERA

OTELLO

GUESS THE CLASSICAL PIECE... FOR PEOPLE WHO DON'T READ MUSIC

1   Gershwin: *Rhapsody in Blue*
2   Herrmann: *Psycho* (score)
3   Brahms: Lullaby
4   John Williams: *Star Wars* (score)
5   Pachelbel: Canon in D
6   Beethoven: Symphony No. 5
7   Tchaikovsky: Dance of the Sugar Plum Fairy (from *The Nutcracker*)
8   Wagner: 'Ride of the Valkyries' (from *Die Walküre*)
9   John Williams: *Jaws* (score)
10   Rossini: *William Tell* Overture

PRESTO

ACROSS

6	Rattle
7	Caro
9	*Gadfly*
10	Tempo
12	Cast
13	*Norma*
17	Eight
18	Jane
21	Laura
22	Norway
24	Ends
25	Pedals

DOWN

1	Strauss
2	Clef
3	Ragtime
4	Dorma
5	Widor
8	Xylophone
11	Act
14	Einaudi
15	Maracas
16	Red
19	Lloyd
20	Queen
23	Rieu

CODA

Conductor is the coded word.

CODE: 1/B, 2/E, 3/A, 4/T, 5/O, 6/S, 7/I, 8/N, 9/Q, 10/K, 11/G, 12/H, 13/Z, 14/R, 15/J, 16/X, 17/Y, 18/F, 19/U, 20/W, 21/P, 22/M, 23/V, 24/L, 25/C, 26/D.

Words formed, reading from left to right and from top to bottom of the grid:

ACROSS	DOWN
Valentine	Obstinate
Beat	Kangaroos
Youngest	Abyss
Tights	Equinox
Nurse	Toga
Formula	Nest
Box	Quizzical
Trooper	Carnation
Dozen	For
Typist	Bewitch
Baguette	Steer
Halo	Jail
Elsewhere	Tube

COMPOSITION

The composer is ZIMMER.

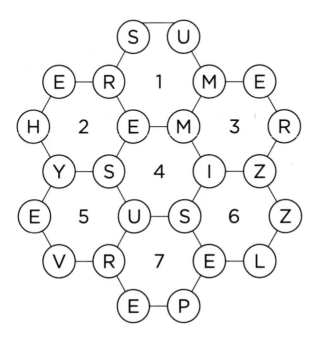

1   Summer
2   Heresy
3   Zimmer
4   Misuse
5   Survey
6   Sizzle
7   Peruse

OPERA OR CHEESE?

1 *Cavalleria rusticana*: **Opera**
2 Époisses de Bourgogne: **Cheese**
3 Bear Hill: **Cheese**
4 *Blue Monday*: **Opera**
5 Casu Marzu: **Cheese**
6 *Platée*: **Opera**
7 Anari: **Cheese**
8 *La Dame Blanche*: **Opera**
9 Passendale: **Cheese**
10 *The Nose*: **Opera**
11 Saga: **Cheese**
12 Scamorza: **Cheese**
13 *Il Re Pastore*: **Opera**
14 *Dalibor:* **Opera**
15 Abbaye de Belloc: **Cheese**
16 Remoudou: **Cheese**
17 *Fidelio*: **Opera**
18 *La Périchole*: **Opera**
19 Fiore Sardo: **Cheese**
20 Västerbottensost: **Cheese**

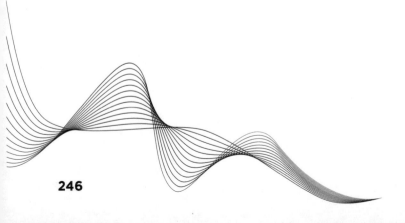

CODA

Clavichord is the coded instrument.

CODE: 1/L, 2/U, 3/T, 4/E, 5/O, 6/Q, 7/N, 8/C, 9/S, 10/A, 11/I, 12/W, 13/Y, 14/J, 15/Z, 16/F, 17/G, 18/K, 19/H, 20/M, 21/B, 22/V, 23/R, 24/D, 25/X, 26/P.

Words formed, reading from left to right and from top to bottom of the grid:

ACROSS
Alabaster
Lute
Bulletin
Quiche
Excel
Overall
Ewe
Costume
Greet
Annexe
Rejected
Jive
Courtyard

DOWN
Eloquence
Staircase
Label
Believe
Seek
Exit
Cafeteria
Flattered
Owe
Empathy
Radar
Zero
Tear

RING CYCLE

1 Elgar
2 Arena
3 Nasal
4 Alibi
5 Bizet
6 Ether
7 Erode
8 Delta
9 Table
10 Level

HIDDEN MUSIC

VESPERS

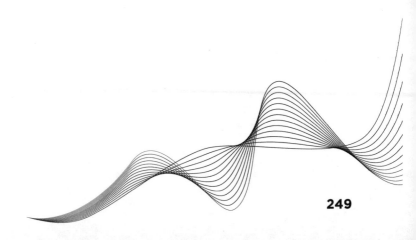

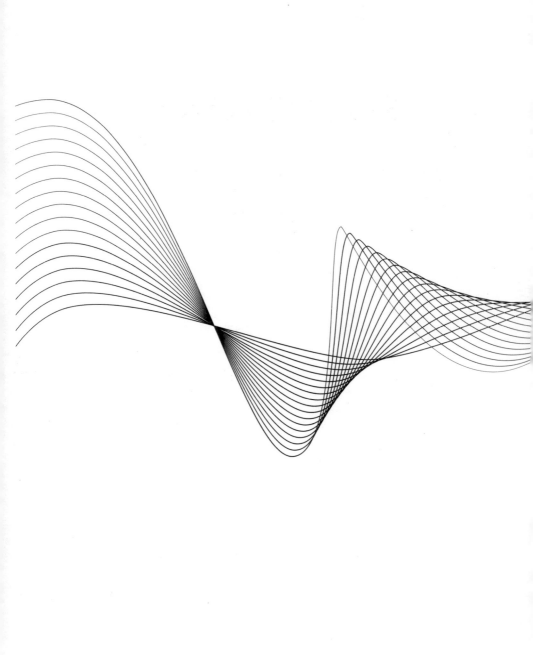

SECTION THREE

MOLTO VIVACE

CAN YOU MATCH THE COMPOSER TO THEIR COUNTRY OF BIRTH?

1   Antonio Vivaldi: (d) Italy. (Antonio Lucio Vivaldi was born in Venice, Italy, on 4 March 1678.)

2   Joaquín Rodrigo: (d) Spain. (Joaquín Rodrigo was born in Sagunto, Valencia, Spain, on 22 November 1901.)

3   Béla Bartók: (d) Hungary. (Béla Viktor János Bartók was born in the small Banatian town of Nagyszentmiklós in the Kingdom of Hungary, Austria-Hungary, on 25 March 1881.)

4   Claude Debussy: (a) France. (Claude Debussy was born in Saint-Germain-en-Laye, Paris, France, on 22 August 1862.)

5   Frédéric Chopin: (c) Poland. (Frédéric François Chopin was born in Warsaw, Poland, on 1 March 1810.)

6   Franz Liszt: (d) Hungary. (Franz Liszt was born in the village of Doborján in Sopron County in the Kingdom of Hungary, Austrian Empire, on 22 October 1811.)

7   John Williams: (a) United States. (John Towner Williams was born in New York, USA, on 8 February 1932.)

8   Antonín Dvořák: (c) Czech Republic. (Antonín Leopold Dvořák was born in Nelahozeves, near Prague, Austrian Empire – present-day Czech Republic – on 8 September 1841.)

9   George Gershwin: (c) United States. (George Jacob Gershwin was of Russian Jewish and Ukrainian Jewish ancestry but born in New York, USA, on 26 September 1898.)

10 Sergei Rachmaninov: (d) Russia. (Sergei Rachmaninov was born at a family estate in the Novgorod province in northwestern Russia on 1 April 1873.)

11 Jean Sibelius: (b) Finland. (Jean Sibelius was born in Hämeenlinna in the Grand Duchy of Finland, an autonomous part of the Russian Empire, on 8 December 1865.)

12   Edward Elgar: (c) England.
(Sir Edward William Elgar was
born in the small village of Lower
Broadheath, near Worcester,
England, on 2 June 1857.)

13   Frederick Delius: (c) England.
(Frederick Theodore Albert Delius
was born in Bradford, Yorkshire,
England, on 29 January 1862.)

14   Wolfgang Amadeus Mozart:
(c) Austria.
(Wolfgang Amadeus Mozart
was born in Salzburg, Austria,
on 27 January 1756 – though it
was only annexed to the Austrian
Empire in 1805. Before that it was
an independent city state.)

15   Sergei Prokofiev: (a) Ukraine.
(Sergei Sergeyevich Prokofiev
was born in Sontsovka, a remote
rural estate in the Yekaterinoslav
Governorate of the Russian Empire
– present-day Ukraine – on 27 April
1891.)

16   Ennio Morricone: (a) Italy.
(Ennio Morricone was born in
Rome, Italy, on 10 November 1928.)

17   Pyotr Tchaikovsky: (b) Russia.
(Pyotr Ilyich Tchaikovsky was
born in Votkinsk, a small town in
Vyatka Governorate – present-day
Udmurtia – on 7 May 1840.)

18   George Frideric Handel:
(b) Germany.
(George Frideric Handel was
born in Halle-on-Saal, Duchy
of Magdeburg, Germany, on
23 February 1685.)

19   Edvard Grieg: (d) Norway.
(Edvard Hagerup Grieg was born
in Bergen, Norway, on 15 June
1843.)

20   Ludwig van Beethoven:
(a) Germany.
(Ludwig van Beethoven was
born in Bonn, Germany, in
December 1770.)

ENIGMA VARIATIONS

ACROSS

7   Colour
9   Operas
10   Diminuendo
11   Solo
12   Beats
13   Keyboards
16   Quavers
21   Contralto
22   Pedal
24   Aria
25   Guitarists
26   Unison
27   Brahms

DOWN

1   Notices
2   Society
3   Trout
4   Koko
5   Messiah
6   Ballade
8   Conservatoire
14   Bars
15   Tuba
17   Soaring
18   Strauss
19   Recital
20   Ragtime
23   Samba
25   Gong

PRESTO

ACROSS

6   Treble
7   Tuba
9   Angela
10   Aaron
12   Ride
13   Sheku
17   Style
18   *Rite*
21   Carol
22   *Elvira*
24   Scat
25   Coates

DOWN

1   Kennedy
2   Blue
3   *Rusalka*
4   Barry
5   Piano
8   Pachelbel
11   Ira
14   Italian
15   Vibrato
16   Met
19   Scale
20   Brass
23   Viol

OCTET

1	Albinoni		15	Viennese
2	Broadway		16	Movement
3	Oratorio		17	Virtuoso
4	*Firebird*		18	American
5	Habanera		19	Gershwin
6	*Swan Lake*		20	Complete
7	Schubert		21	Composer
8	Paganini		22	Twenties
9	Baritone		23	Cassette
10	Rehearse		24	Applause
11	*Miserere*		25	Soloists
12	'Cavatina'		26	Audition
13	Wireless		27	Quartets
14	Semitone		28	Libretto

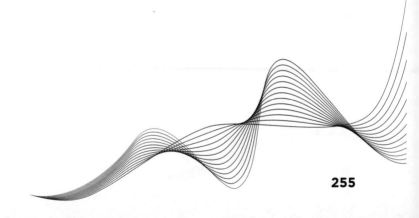

CAN YOU COMPLETE THE FAMOUS QUOTE FROM EACH COMPOSER?

1 Claude Debussy: (b) art
2 Leonard Bernstein: (a) time
3 Béla Bartók: (b) horses
4 Igor Stravinsky: (a) steal
5 Edward Elgar: (a) God
6 Johannes Brahms: (b) craftsmanship
7 Joseph Haydn: (c) confuse
8 J S Bach: (c) industrious
9 Erik Satie: (a) proudest
10 Robert Schumann: (b) duty
11 Dmitri Shostakovich: (a) satisfied
12 John Cage: (c) frightened
13 Giacomo Puccini: (b) Inspiration
14 Richard Wagner: (b) Imagination

METRONOME

1   Blue
2   *Peer*
3   Rule
4   Prom
5   Hero
6   Slur
7   Amen
8   Rose
9   Arts
10   Butt

SESTET

1   Violin
2   Rounds
3   Walton
4   *Choice*
5   Prague
6   Albert
7   Nicola
8   Choral
9   String
10   Berlin
11   Unison
12   Repeat

CAN YOU NAME ALL THESE CLEFS?

1   (a) Treble
2   (a) Alto
3   (b) Bass
4   (c) Tenor
5   (a) Baritone
6   (c) French violin
7   (a) Percussion
8   (b) Soprano
9   (d) Octave
10   (d) Subbass

CAN YOU TRANSLATE THESE BASIC ITALIAN MUSICAL TERMS?

1   (a) Andante: A moderately fast piece of music
2   (c) Fermata: A prolonged note
3   (b) Tremolo: A rapid back and forth movement on the same note
4   (a) Cantabile: In a singable fashion
5   (c) Ritardando: Slow down gradually
6   (a) Diminuendo: Gradually get quieter
7   (b) Cadenza: A virtuoso solo passage
8   (c) Da Capo: From the beginning
9   (c) Basso continuo: Figured bass
10   (b) Giocoso: Playfully
11   (a) Ostinato: A musical phrase which persistently repeats
12   (c) Presto: In a quick tempo

TEST YOUR KNOWLEDGE OF MUSIC NOTATION

1. (c) c.2000 BC
2. (a) Neumes
3. (d) Bipunctum
4. (a) 5
5. (a) Accidentals
6. (a) Tremolo
7. (c) Up bow this note
8. (d) A demisharp
9. (b) We just made it up
10. (a) A three-quarter-tone flat
11. (b) Two hundred fifty-sixth note
12. (d) Fa sol la ti
13. (d) 5
14. (a) **1**

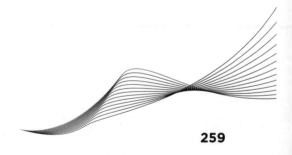

ENIGMA VARIATIONS

ACROSS

7   Caruso
9   Steven
10 Palestrina
11 Lost
12 Delay
13 Emotional
16 Touring
21 Freelance
22 Pears
24 Fair
25 Summertime
26 Delius
27 Sonata

DOWN

1   Cabaret
2   Funeral
3   Forte
4   Asia
5   Berlioz
6   Persian
8   Eric Morecambe
14 Tuna
15 Coda
17 Created
18 Refrain
19 Setting
20 Promote
23 Verse
25 Sash

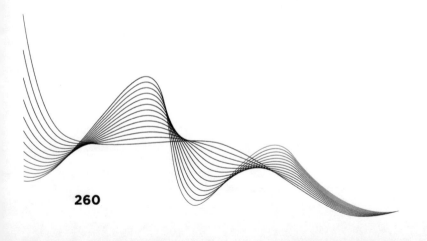

HEXACHORDS

1   Barber
2   Brazil
3   Double
4   Melody
5   Treble
6   Series
7   Sharps
8   Tracks
9   Spinet
10   *Enigma*
11   Season
12   Renown

METRONOME

1   Girl
2   Clap
3   Aria
4   Open
5   Fate
6   Lilt
7   *Snow*
8   Memo
9   Item
10   Glee

OCTET

1	*Rhapsody*	15	Danseuse
2	*Fantasia*	16	Estonian
3	Workshop	17	Musician
4	Ludovico	18	Bassoons
5	Synopsis	19	*Turandot*
6	Clarinet	20	Minor key
7	Hymn Book	21	*Pictures*
8	Concerto	22	Ad libbed
9	Arranger	23	*Sorcerer*
10	Arpeggio	24	Organist
11	Preludes	25	Princess
12	Jurassic	26	Minstrel
13	Thieving	27	Gardiner
14	Reissued	28	Recorder

ENIGMA VARIATIONS

ACROSS

7	Sleigh
9	Adagio
10	Engagement
11	Side
12	Study
13	Beethoven
16	Patrons
21	Crossbows
22	Baton
24	Emma
25	Didgeridoo
26	Pearls
27	Albert

DOWN

1	Planets
2	Vivaldi
3	Sheet
4	Cast
5	Bassoon
6	Fiddler
8	*The Merry Widow*
14	Tone
15	Lamb
17	Trumpet
18	Astaire
19	Marimba
20	Colours
23	Regal
25	Disc

HOW WELL DO YOU KNOW THE FIRST NAMES OF THE GREAT COMPOSERS?

1   (d) Ludwig van Beethoven
2   (a) Bedrich Smetana
3   (d) Pyotr Tchaikovsky
4   (d) Philip Glass
5   (a) Franz Liszt
6   (c) Gaetano Donizetti
7   (b) Arcangelo Corelli
8   (d) Johannes Brahms
9   (a) Claude Debussy
10 (c) Jean Sibelius

SESTET

1   Zither
2   Wilson
3   *Isolde*
4   Yehudi
5   Lament
6   Toured
7   Minims
8   Legato
9   Claude
10 Brahms
11 Prince
12 Gifted

THE HARDEST EVER MOZART QUIZ

1   (b) Johannes Chrysostomus Wolfgangus Theophilus Mozart
2   (b) Nannerl
3   (a) Eight
4   (c) Orestes
5   (b) 23
6   (b) Gottlieb Stephanie
7   (c) Aloysia Weber
8   (a) Birdcatcher
9   (d) Glass harmonica

HOW WELL DO YOU KNOW YOUR MUSICAL NICKNAMES?

1 (a) 'Raindrop' is the nickname for a Chopin piano prelude.
2 (b) 'Envelope' is a completely random word.
3 (a) 'Toy' is the nickname for Mozart's Cassation in G major.
4 (a) 'London' is the nickname for Haydn's Symphony No. 104.
5 (a) 'Emperor' is the nickname for Beethoven's Piano Concerto No. 5.
6 (b) 'Milan' is a completely random word.
7 (a) 'Nordic' is the nickname for Hanson's Symphony No. 1.
8 (b) 'Sunrise' is a completely random word.
9 (b) 'State' is a completely random word.
10 (a) 'Trout' is the nickname for Schubert's Piano Quintet.
11 (b) 'Ship' is a completely random word.
12 (b) 'Stroll' is a completely random word.
13 (b) 'Mountain' is a completely random word.
14 (a) 'Concord' is the nickname for Ives's Piano Sonata No. 2.
15 (b) 'Cow' is a completely random word.
16 (a) 'Ocean' is the nickname for Rubinstein's Symphony No. 2.
17 (b) 'Box' is a completely random word.
18 (a) 'Butterfly' is the nickname for Chopin's Étude op. 25, No. 9.
19 (a) 'Surprise' is the nickname for Haydn's Symphony No. 94.
20 (a) 'Jupiter' is the nickname for Holst's Suite op. 32, No. 4.

QUIZ CROSSWORD

ACROSS

7 *Kismet*
9 Lyrics
10 Metronomes
11 Deaf
12 Clock
13 Moviegoer
15 Portray
20 Cleopatra
21 Verse
23 Tell
24 Tin whistle
25 Writer
26 Minuet

DOWN

1 *Giselle*
2 America
3 Stand
4 Classical
5 Prodigy
6 Octaves
8 *Game of Thrones*
14 *Monastery*
16 Allegro
17 Jollity
18 *Seasons*
19 Psalter
22 Chime

HEXACHORDS

1 Andrew
2 Webber
3 Revels
4 Billed
5 Alison
6 Oberon
7 Hector
8 Venice
9 Minute
10 Kettle
11 Mickey
12 Nimrod

METRONOME

1 *Babe*
2 Reed
3 Oboe
4 *Edge*
5 Berg
6 Moor
7 Peru
8 Igor
9 Trio
10 *Così*

OCTET

1 *Aranjuez*
2 *La Bohème*
3 Tuneless
4 Ensemble
5 Fandango
6 Keyboard
7 Serenade
8 Abridged
9 *Gaslight*
10 Mandolin
11 Sibelius
12 Laughing
13 *Carnival*
14 Virginal
15 Egyptian
16 Scriabin
17 Crooning
18 Operetta
19 Pianists
20 Finalist
21 Staccato
22 Fanfares
23 Carillon
24 *Casanova*
25 Acoustic
26 Protégée
27 Madrigal
28 Stirring

QUIZ CROSSWORD

ACROSS

7	Tenors
9	Rutter
10	Coloratura
11	Post
12	Minim
13	Mediaeval
15	Tippett
20	Semibreve
21	Fugue
23	Open
24	Threepenny
25	Presto
26	Leader

DOWN

1	Segovia
2	Borodin
3	Oscar
4	Organists
5	Stephen
6	*Messiah*
8	Giuseppe Verdi
14	Librettos
16	*Vespers*
17	Finnish
18	Funeral
19	Quintet
22	Cello

WHAT CAUSED THE DEATH OF THESE CLASSICAL COMPOSERS?

1   (j) Jean-Baptiste Lully
2   (e) Henry Purcell
3   (b) Alexander Scriabin
4   (c) Anton Webern
5   (f) Ernest Chausson
6   (l) Enrique Granados
7   (k) Charles-Valentin Alkan
8   (h) Louis Vierne
9   (d) Sergei Prokofiev
10 (i) Alexander Borodin
11 (a) César Franck
12 (g) Arnold Schoenberg

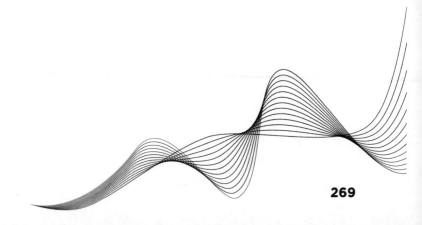

THE ULTIMATE BEETHOVEN QUIZ

1   (c) 1770
2   (c) Johann
3   (a) Five
4   (b) After a fit of rage at being interrupted while working, he fell and subsequently rose to find that he was deaf
5   (c) No. 21
6   (c) Napoleon Bonaparte
7   (b) Friedrich Schiller
8   (a) Symphony No. 9
9   (a) Florestan
10   (b) Six
11   (b) C minor
12   (a) Vienna

HEXACHORDS

1   Delius
2   Toured
3   Russia
4   Danish
5   Finale
6   Defeat
7   Quoted
8   Loudly
9   Lively
10   Review
11   Father
12   Guitar

SESTET

1   Handel
2   France
3   Encore
4   Bridge
5   Winner
6   *Salome*
7   Patron
8   *Eroica*
9   Golden
10   London
11   Sleeve
12   George

THE ULTIMATE CLASSICAL MUSIC QUIZ

1   (c) Tragic
2   (a) Variation XI (G.R.S.)
3   (b) Oxford
4   (b) Sir Malcolm Sargent
5   (b) 60
6   (a) Chalumeau
7   (c) Teacups on a string
8   (a) Wolfgang Amadeus Mozart
9   (b) Prompter
10   (a) Denis

11   (c) *The Slave of Duty*
12   (b) Brahms
13   (c) India
14   (d) Hovercraft
15   (a) 4
16   (d) Simon Callow
17   (a) Carthage
18   (c) 1973
19   (b) Sir Walter Parratt
20   (d) Madonna

METRONOME

1 Muse
2 Lead
3 *Asia*
4 Idea
5 Dame
6 Film
7 Walt
8 Peal
9 Emma
10 Plum

HEXACHORDS

1 Robert
2 Resume
3 Cinema
4 Ticket
5 Rattle
6 Hebrew
7 *Beauty*
8 Stuart
9 Themes
10 Bremen
11 Skater
12 Dvořák

QUIZ CROSSWORD

ACROSS

7　Gloria
9　Imogen
10　Drumsticks
11　Loud
12　*Peter*
13　Harmonies
15　Fiddles
20　Christmas
21　Pearl
23　Opus
24　Ron Goodwin
25　Vienna
26　Dunbar

DOWN

1　Slurred
2　*Trumpet*
3　Waltz
4　Midsummer
5　Poulenc
6　Requiem
8　Richard Wagner
14　Victorian
16　Chaplin
17　*Missing*
18　Wedding
19　Arrival
22　Rondo

THE CLASSICAL MUSIC GENERAL KNOWLEDGE QUIZ

1　(a) Buxtehude
2　(b) Knitting
3　(d) 175
4　(b) 140
5　(b) He only ate white food
6　(a) A pencil and manuscript
7　(b) Mozart
8　(d) Beethoven
9　(b) He commissioned the Tonhalle Orchester Zürich to perform one of his compositions for her on their staircase
10　(b) Rodolfo

OCTET

1	Overture	15	Crotchet
2	Comeback	16	Williams
3	*Superman*	17	Folk song
4	Yodeller	18	Scottish
5	*War Horse*	19	Strummed
6	Nocturne	20	Farewell
7	Plectrum	21	*Star Trek*
8	Trombone	22	*Imperial*
9	Vocalist	23	Sequence
10	*Traviata*	24	Toreador
11	Falsetto	25	Promoter
12	Platform	26	Berceuse
13	Side drum	27	Benjamin
14	Passages	28	Duettist

ENIGMA VARIATIONS

ACROSS:

7	Figaro
9	Atonal
10	'The Tempest'
11	Pace
12	Green
13	Plainsong
16	Giselle
21	Norwegian
22	Bleak
24	Rows
25	Squeeze box
26	Silent
27	Pirate

DOWN

1	Richard
2	Partner
3	*Norma*
4	Part
5	Compose
6	Balcony
8	The Blue Danube
14	Isle
15	Sing
17	Borodin
18	Two step
19	Allegro
20	Gavotte
23	Tempo
25	Sets

QUIZ CROSSWORD

ACROSS

7   Legato
9   Adrian
10 Grand Opera
11 Bass
12 Piano
13 Bluebeard
15 Gondola
20 Recorders
21 Light
23 Glad
24 Clavichord
25 *Boléro*
26 Gretel

DOWN

1   Refrain
2   Cannons
3   Solos
4   Bagatelle
5   Trebles
6   Maestro
8   *Die Fledermaus*
14 Conductor
16 Berlioz
17 Soldier
18 Michael
19 Charles
22 Binge

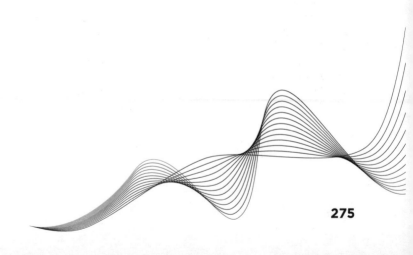

A QUIZ FOR CLASSICAL MUSIC EXPERTS

1   (b) D flat major
2   (d) Hitting the strings with the wooden side of your violin bow
3   (c) Flute, oboe, clarinet, horn and bassoon
4   (a) Fade away
5   (c) Dorian
6   (a) 9
7   (c) G sharp minor
8   (d) Sibelius
9   (a) A minor
10   (b) Elektra chord

SESTET

1   Mozart
2   *Caesar*
3   Caruso
4   *Camera*
5   Stress
6   Poland
7   Sonata
8   Tattoo
9   *Eugene*
10   Casals
11   Stereo
12   Raised